PILLS, PO...

Addic...

Contents

Acknowledgments

Words are inadequate to express apppreciation for so many people who have loved me and prayed me into the positive experiences inherent in these pages.

In practical terms, thanks are due to Elaine Brewer, who patiently typed at least three manuscripts, and Jo Cropp who graciously provided a base as an oasis of reflection and solitude.

To every person who ever worked with Yeldall Christian Centres – staff, wives, families, board members, committee members, volunteers. Only eternity will ever fully reveal what your sacrifices have wrought, but you have blessed me and mine so sweetly and richly. **Thank you.**

1

The World is a Psychoactive Pic-'n'-Mix Sweet Shop

A while back I visited a jail in New York. I walked through the cell block with a cop I've known for years. A kid in one of the cells called to me.

'Mister, I gotta talk to you. I need help, please talk to me.'

'What's the problem, son?' I asked. 'What can I do for you?'

He lowered his voice so my friend could not hear. 'I've been here seven days already, and they won't let me call my father. Please, I'll give you the number. Call my father. Tell him I'm in trouble. I need him.'

He was in trouble all right, but his father would never be able to help him. The cop told me the story. This boy was a nice kid, never been in trouble before. College student, upper-middle-class. He smoked marijuana, but was not considered a heavy smoker. A couple of months ago he was hit with 'angel dust'. Someone had stuffed a joint that he smoked with it. After the party, he walked into the house where he lived with his family, took a gun out of his father's desk drawer, went into his parents' bedroom, and killed them both. Then he killed his little sister.

He does not know they are dead. He does not remember killing them. He had been in jail for two months and every day he cried for his father to come and help him.[1]

Thankfully stories like this are incredibly rare, but they still highlight the issues involved. The fact is that the result of 'innocent' drug-taking brings heartache and tragedy not only to the individuals who do it, but also to their families.

Why the problem?

Availability and price

'Young people today appear to see themselves as consumers in a psychoactive pic-'n'-mix sweet shop, starting with and staying with alcohol ... but then trying cannabis, "poppers" and LSD blotters.' These words of Professor Howard Parker are supported by research which 'continues to document unprecedented drug use among the school age population'.[2]

Statistics confirm that among fourteen- and fifteen-year-olds in the north-west of England, 59 per cent have been offered drugs, and 36 per cent have actually tried them.[3] In Exeter the figure is slightly lower – 31 per cent have tried them.[4] A 1993 Home Office report says that use of the drug 'ecstasy' has increased by 700 per cent in the past few years, while one in three young people who go to 'raves' have tried drugs.

Prices of drugs are low, especially compared with the price of alcohol; kids can pool their money and for less than the price of a packet of cigarettes each one can get 'stoned'. The effects will vary from person to person, but a 'trip' can last either minutes or hours. And it isn't only illegal drugs that are a problem for young people, because alcohol is readily available on every street corner. Its consumption is encouraged by adults – as exemplified by young delegates at a conference on alcohol abuse being served wine and spirits at their hotel!

One of the major reasons for such addiction is that parents, like their children, have grown up in a world where instant gratification is seen as everyone's inalienable right:

> We live in a world of cheap, quick thrills. You can get a quarter pounder in less than two minutes, guaranteed. Sit on the couch and, with a punch on the remote control, turn on the music, the TV or the VCR. Take a pill and, within minutes, clear out your sinuses, settle your stomach or simply lose your appetite. It is all so simple. Partake and dispose. A thrill or a cure a minute.[5]

Perhaps the greatest reason for the growing drug epidemic is that, in many people's minds, drugs are socially acceptable. Drugs and alcohol are not only a readily acceptable part of their own social scene, but are increasingly approved of by the 'establishment'. Today's teenagers see growing evidence that many adults accept drugs in their attitude to what used to be the great unmentionables:

- **Criminality** Young people see that possession of certain drugs is allowed by some police forces.

- **Legalisation** There is a very vocal minority group of people who want to legalise certain drugs. This will clear the way for unrestrained use of these drugs as far as young people are concerned.

- **The 'Cannabis is harmless' debate** Once again, a vocal minority who want to justify their own abuse of cannabis have taken the moral high ground. Using the distorted and unproven logic that cannabis is not as dangerous as alcohol, they have communicated to young people the message that so-called 'soft' drugs will not harm them.

- **Harm minimisation** This is the accepted way of helping people to limit the amount of damage they do to themselves or other people. In its basic form it involves: (1) prescribing drugs that people would normally buy on the 'black market'; (2) supplying as many clean syringes and needles as people need to prevent them using other people's equipment, thereby reducing the risk of spreading HIV/AIDS.

In themselves, these measures sound perfectly reasonable, but the danger is that young people will see them as a justification for carrying on using drugs. Harm minimisation conveys the message that regardless of the risk of using drugs, someone will provide a damage-limitation exercise that will ensure they won't suffer the consequences of their drug abuse.

Who is at risk?

I have spent nearly fifteen years working with drug addicts and alcoholics, trying to work out why people get addicted. I can't write about the reasons, and the answers to the problem, without referring to real people – people like Noel, Campbell, 'Scouse', Ken, John, Alastair, and many others. These are the ones who broke free, but then there are those who died, often alone in public toilets or dirty squats, people like John V, Rob, Vince and Phil.

All of these men's lives began with the promise inherent in everyone's life. They were normal in every sense of the word, and I knew them all as very special, highly intelligent and sensitive individuals. Each one of them was born with the potential to achieve far more than they or their parents ever imagined. They could each have been a president or a nuclear scientist! Yet somewhere along the line something went wrong – long before drugs ever came into their lives. I have had the privilege of being deeply involved in many of their lives, as they have shared intimately details of how and why they found themselves addicted.

A few were abused sexually, or through physical or verbal violence, but the majority grew up in relatively normal homes. However, behind their comments about how they felt as they grew up there is something really chilling in terms of emotional deprivation:

'Basically, I was never accepted for what I was.'
'I felt lonely, inadequate, never really part of the family.'
'I was never prepared for adult life, it was such a shock.'
'Being constantly told I was a failure.'
'Loved one minute and not the next.'
'No support, no advice – nothing.'
'Unwanted, punished, hated and neglected.'
'Being constantly told how much of an unwanted accident my existence was.'
'How I would never amount to anything.'

British Library Cataloguing in Publication Data
A record for this book is available from the British Library

ISBN 0 340 65637 9

Printed and bound in Great Britain by
Cox & Wyman Ltd, Reading, Berkshire

Hodder and Stoughton Ltd
A Division of Hodder Headline PLC
338 Euston Road
London NW1 3BH

Pills, Poppers and Caffeine

Addiction and Your Family

David Partington

Hodder & Stoughton

LONDON SYDNEY AUCKLAND TORONTO

It is hardly surprising, given the circumstances that surrounded these men's lives, that once drugs became available they felt inclined to try them. The majority had already begun smoking cigarettes, so it was an easy transition to something else, especially cannabis. That first experiment with illegal drugs, or even alcohol, almost invariably happened in a friendly environment. For many, it was often after a game of football, or something else equally innocent. They sat in a circle, and the bottle or 'joint' was passed around and everyone else joined in. In one sense, they had little choice about whether they took part or not:

1 Every other person on whom he or she depended for friendship and acceptance had already indulged and they didn't want to be different.

2 They had heard about what happens when you take drugs, and were curious. They were dissatisfied with life in general and wanted some 'kicks'.

The initial effect of taking a drug, of snorting, of swallowing a pill or taking a swig, was for most of them pleasant. Yet any pleasurable feelings were often obliterated by sheer terror or overwhelming guilt. They went home totally convinced that someone would accuse them of being a 'junkie'. Nothing happened, though, other than that they made the decision that they would never again take drugs. Then one day they found themselves in a similar environment where they had the opportunity to try the same drug or something different. For some, it was an easy decision to 'use' a second time, made more attractive by the remembrance of the satisfying 'buzz' they got last time. There was also the fact that for some, in addition to the nice warm glow they had experienced, they also had the freedom, for the first time ever, to chat up a person of the opposite sex. It didn't matter what the rationale or reason was, the fact of life was that once you had taken drugs the first time, it was easier the second time, and even easier the third . . .

So there they were, on the slide into addiction, and carried on down it at varying speeds, depending upon their temperament, friends, availability of drugs, money and opportunity.

Family heartbreak

On the way down the slide, the fallout on the rest of the family will only be fully apparent to you if there is someone in your family who is addicted. For some, there is the slowly unfolding tragedy of seeing their child go through the different stages of drug abuse and addiction. The impact on them personally is very profound, affecting them not only financially, but also physically, mentally, emotionally and spiritually. They experience increasingly spiteful and vicious confrontations, as well as knowing that they are being conned and manipulated. That their child is actually stealing from them and other members of the family becomes a fact of life. The damage to other people and relationships, especially within the family, is severe and heart-wrenching. Everyone gets drawn into involvement with social workers, doctors, probation officers and the police in a way they never ever dreamed of.

Addiction claims the life not only of the addict but of the rest of the family too. Ahead is the potential of a lifetime of heartbreak, as they slide deeper and deeper into the despair of addiction.

2

The Slide into Addiction

For many people the thought of becoming addicted is either totally inexcusable or a ridiculous notion. The truth, however, is not as simple as it looks and that is why we must all be very careful not to make rash judgments. Addiction is not something which happens instantaneously, but creeps up on us unawares. As one addict said, 'The killer for me was the physical pleasure. Heroin has the most tremendously physical effect. You take the stuff; all you are aware of is an extremely pleasant and friendly sensation, but a very, very intense one ... So I thought, yes, more.'

It is this desire for a repeat of such an intensely pleasurable and exciting sensation that is one of the main reasons why young people become addicted. A government research paper confirms that other common reasons quoted are 'to feel big', 'to show off', 'to look grown-up', and 'because it's trendy'.

Whatever you and I may think about the horrors of addiction, drugs – especially for young people – are not only a source of pleasure but they can also blank out the hassle and problems of adolescence. This, incidentally, is one of the major reasons why addiction is so difficult to deal with. The fact is that because a teenager is 'cushioned' by drugs from the hard knocks of life, he or she never really grows up. As a consequence, their emotional and social development goes into 'neutral'; and addicts carry with them, throughout their drug-taking history and beyond, their adolescent attitudes and perceptions. They remain immature and inadequate until such time as they find the right environment of acceptance and 'tough' love (see p. 55) where they can go through the adolescent process without drugs, and find real freedom.

If you really want to understand the process further, place yourself in the position of a young drug-user who is part of a dynamic and fast-moving subculture. You are also part of the music, the loose morals and the increasingly antisocial attitudes. Each person you mix with not only shares your immature attitudes, but reinforces them along the lines of:

• The world really does owe us a living.

• Getting something for nothing is 'success'.

• All is fair in love and war.

• It is more blessed to get than to give.

• Whatever is yours is mine, especially if you are insured!

However, as the need grows to find the money for an ever-increasing quantity of drugs, life becomes uncomfortable. It brings with it not only growing despair, but also the hostility of family, statutory authorities, police, courts, hospitals and prisons. The result is the development of an elaborate defence mechanism to protect you, as far as possible, from reality. Every problem you have is someone else's problem, and you make sure others know it so that you can be certain the guilt is transferred to them. Yet despite this, you slowly but surely realise that life on the drug scene is not quite as attractive as it first appeared:

• You increasingly recognise that you are developing a tolerance, so that you need more drugs, and more often, to achieve the same effect.

• Your life increasingly revolves around getting your next fix, just to stop the discomfort involved in 'withdrawing'.

• Stealing and crime have generally become non-optional, with your parents being the first victims.

- Your health deteriorates, not least because the drugs you are pumping into your body are toxic.

- Deep down, you still feel just as lonely, inadequate, rejected and unloved.

- Despite a longing to be free, you find yourself subject to a powerful psychological 'compulsion' to carry on using your chosen drug.

Age is no barrier to addiction

Older age groups get addicted for many of the same reasons that younger people do: they find that alcohol or drugs cover up the pain of childhood, or even the feelings of adult rejection. They too find that drugs cushion them from heartache, a deep sense of inadequacy, inferiority, despair and bitterness. Often, their addiction began with a doctor allowing tranquillisers to be prescribed beyond the 'safe' period – about four to six weeks. For others, it was one gin and tonic a day, which became two, three, four ... and beyond. Behind it all was the despair and pressure created by events such as:

- Long-standing relationships falling apart.

- Children failing to live up to your large investment of money.

- The long-awaited promotion that fails to materialise.

- Redundancy or unemployment.

- Ever-increasing stress at work.

- The feeling of being trapped at home by young children or aged parents.

- People coming home too tired to be bothered to pay any attention to their partner's needs.

- Taking second place to a partner's career.

The process of addiction

Very few people become addicts immediately. The vast majority go through a process involving three different stages:

- Experimental or casual use.
- Misuse or abuse.
- Addiction.

Stage one: experimental or casual use

Casual drug-users try out or experiment with a substance in much the same way that people drink alcohol socially. Some have a bad experience, but others feel pleasure and enjoy it. Eventually, having convinced themselves that no harm is done, such people quickly begin to learn how and when to use the drug in order to make the experience more intense.

It would be difficult to stop a drug-user at this stage, because (apart from the pleasure they experience) they have convinced themselves that they are the one exception to the rule – *they* will never become an addict.

Stage two: misuse or abuse

The casual user never sets out to become a drug misuser or problem drinker. Such a change may take months, even years, but the person will slowly but surely feel a growing need to experience the high or euphoria by increasing either the frequency or the amount of drugs or alcohol. They often begin to 'use' outside the normally acceptable social rules, while still initially maintaining some self-imposed control – e.g. never drinking before 10 a.m.! They also develop a growing tolerance to the drugs or alcohol – i.e. they need a higher dose to get the same effect.

Outward signs result from the turmoil within. Verbal aggression towards others, sometimes accompanied by physical violence, becomes an option for a few. For others, their lifestyle becomes more promiscuous and other life values or rules are regularly broken. Addicts may begin to inject at this stage, whereas once they swore blind that that was the one thing they would never do. Drinkers will increasingly choose to get drunk on their own.

They readily recognise that they need to control their misuse, but while they are 'long' on good ideas (particularly about when and how they will give up), they are 'short' on action. Reinforced by their friends, such people rationalise and justify almost every action, especially their abuse of other people. It really is very difficult to talk such misusers into sustained action. What can you offer them that is better? They may well know that they are losing their self-respect, but who wants to experience the intense discomfort that follows when they stop?

It's for all these reasons that it is extremely important to confirm your love and acceptance of them as individuals while making it clear that you reject their drug or alcohol misuse and their behaviour. It is also important to talk to them about ways in which you and other people can help them to rebuild their lives when they *do* make the decision – when they take the first step.

Stage three: addiction

Addiction is when the drugs or alcohol 'use' the addict or alcoholic. People at this stage cannot control themselves or the amount they take; they are enslaved, in bondage. Addicts will do anything to avoid the psychological and physical discomfort of withdrawal. By now, they are probably experiencing a depressingly chaotic lifestyle involving a round of hospitalisation, accidental drug overdoses, social stigma, crime, arrest, prison and family conflict.

They are in a nightmare world where their whole life is dominated by the substance that they crave, in a way that most people cannot possibly imagine. They will do *anything* to carry on using, regardless of how degrading or depraved it is to them or anyone else who gets in the way. Every aspect of life is dominated by the substance – be it relationships, work (if they still have a job), social life, health, sleep, or eating. Addiction is one of the loneliest, most desperate and agonising places to be, and the only way a person has of coping with it seems simple: taking the next fix or the next bottle.

There is yet one further tragedy about addiction, though, that needs to be understood. No matter how often the addict or alcoholic makes the choice to give up, they have before them one of the highest mountains that anyone ever has to climb. That mountain is the one that leads to 'normal' life. Addicts know that it will take days, weeks and months – maybe even years – of hard slog, of real and sustained effort. They know it will need guts and courage that they believe they are totally lacking after they have become a junkie. They have been told for years that all they need to do is 'say no', and they know it's not as easy as that. So they need your help in order to take the first step up that mountain. It may be that you don't feel you can help anyone to take that first step. It's even possible that you have helped them take that first step so often and they have always failed. Maybe you have been hurt too often to find the courage that's needed. I fully understand this, but there's still hope – as one young man's story shows.

> I used to go around with a group of friends. We would smoke 'pot', and occasionally take 'speed' [amphetamines]. Looking back, there were some good laughs. Everyone in my circle took drugs. One day I couldn't get any cannabis: someone suggested I try heroin. I was about eighteen at the time.
>
> It didn't take long before I was totally hooked. After a year or so, I went and registered with a doctor. He gave me methadone, which kept me out of trouble for a while. In time, however, I used other drugs and got an even bigger habit, and my life really hit the rocks. I was working as a motor mechanic. Gradually I was having more time off and I lost my job. Soon my nice flat, car and everything I owned had gone. Whatever I could sell had been sold, and I used to steal from anyone just to satisfy my craving for drugs.

A heroin addict is totally self-centred – I'd steal off my best friend just to get a 'fix'. You wake up in the morning, and your first thought is – money. The questions you ask yourself are, 'Where can I get the money from?' and 'Where can I get the best deal?' There are no holidays, no days off; every day is the same miserable existence.

Eventually, this young man was advised to have a period at Yeldall Manor, a Christian residential rehabilitation centre, and fifteen months later he had virtually completed the programme. His status as 'senior resident' allowed him special privileges, including the opportunity of spending a weekend at home in Scotland. However, on his first day at home, he met all his old friends and, in his own words, 'blew it'. He came back to Yeldall Manor to pick up his belongings; there was to be no more rehabilitation – and no more Christianity:

The director asked me to come into the meeting before I left. He read from the Bible about 'confessing your sins'. I shared with the other lads what I had done, and wept in front of them. They began to weep with me. Later that day, for the first time in my life, I shared with a counsellor about the hatred I felt for my mother, who had once been an alcoholic. As a young boy, I would come home from school and find her lying flat out on the floor.

I loved my mother, but hated the drink problem. I couldn't look her in the eye or talk to her. That night I prayed that I might be able to forgive her. The next night she telephoned and said, 'I want you to forgive me for all the hurt I have caused you.' In a standoffish way, I replied, 'OK – I'll forgive you,' and put the phone down. I went back to my room and began to weep before God. Now I knew that I had to forgive her. Immediately I rang back and apologised for my hatred, and asked her to forgive me, and we wept together.

That was a turning point for me. I'd accepted Christ while at Yeldall, but I'd struggled all along. Now I forgave her, gave my life totally to Christ – and found real freedom.[1]

This man has been totally free of his addiction for very many years now. His life is a testimony to what can happen when people really care, and provide an environment in which real change can take place.

3

Parent Power – Prevention

I believe the stage is set for the Western world to lose a generation to drugs unless parents start to take their responsibilities very seriously. I am convinced that 'parent power' has got to dictate the agenda at home, in schools and in society in general. Why? Because it's not a question of *if* your child is going to be offered drugs, but *when*! You may comfort yourself with the fact that the drug they are offered may only be nicotine or alcohol, but you've read how much damage even they can do.

Prevention must become the single most important word in our vocabulary when it comes to drugs and young people. Preparing our children to say 'yes' to a drug-free lifestyle and 'no' to drugs is of paramount importance. It is never too early to start talking about how they can say 'no', for the age at which schoolchildren are coming into contact with drugs is getting lower all the time. One Oxford newspaper reported a policeman saying, 'I recently spoke to an eight-year-old who told me how he had watched his ten-year-old friends smoking cannabis. He obviously knew what the stuff was, how much it cost, and even where to get it.'[1]

Then there was the mother who, following a crisis, sat down to talk with her children, a boy of ten and a girl of eight. She told of how they talked about drugs with a matter-of-fact knowledge that was startling. They spoke about how there was a small group (in their junior school) who regularly smoked cannabis, which they got from their elder brothers and sisters. They told how some did 'trips'. 'Oh, you know, Mummy, it's speed or ecstasy.' They were vague about the source of these drugs, but explained that everybody in the playground knew who had them, and you could buy what you wanted with your pocket money. Most of their friends didn't buy drugs, they said, because it was too scary if teachers or parents found out. But they told her that some of their playmates regularly sniffed correction fluid, butane lighter gas or even aerosols.[2]

Pushers in the playground

Have you ever thought through the implication of why so many secondary schools are expelling children? It is happening in so many places – Croydon, Bury, Newcastle, Manchester, Wanstead – but why? It is because drugs are becoming part of the lives of these schoolchildren. A report in *The Times* communicated the facts:

> In my school, Mum, about 80 per cent of the pupils are taking or have taken some sort of drug. It's hard not to. You can buy speed, hash and 'trips' from other boys. People smoke speed, they do not inject things because that's considered a bit serious. You always buy from people you know, otherwise you get skanked [conned] and find you've spent, say, £50 on half an ounce of hash, and they've given you less. Half an ounce can keep you going for a month, so you buy it to sell again and make extra money to go to the movies or a club or something. If people buy for themselves, they usually buy one-eighth of an ounce. Cocaine you can't get from school, but people go to Brixton to get it, most people smoke it; they don't snort because your nose gets screwed up.[3]

The report goes on to talk about a complex set of 'rules' that govern who takes what, how and when. Sixteen-year-olds are too sophisticated to bother with solvents – that's for kids. They work hard at covering up for one another even if someone they don't like is stoned and acting strangely. Sometimes they play up themselves in order to confuse the teacher.

No village is untouched

For those who want to find them, drugs are available in every village, town and city in all the countries in the Western world. By all means be comforted by the words 'for those who want to find them', but remember that there are some smart young people out there who want to find your child and persuade them that drugs are fun.

Prevention: parent power in action

Prevention is all about giving our children the security and the facts about drugs that will lead them to make the decision to say 'no' to drugs or alcohol abuse, and 'yes' to a healthy lifestyle. Young people themselves have some very clear ideas about prevention. One group of sixteen- to eighteen-year-old girls made some interesting comments after one prevention talk:

'Speaking plainly, telling the truth and being honest was really helpful.'

'A more personal emphasis rather than factual information really helped me.'

'A more open and less alarmist attitude makes a real difference to my response.'

'You understand the vulnerability of teenage years.'

'Talk some more about peer pressure, please.'

'You weren't patronising.'

'You didn't treat us like overprotected children.'

This group of bright, intelligent young women communicated what they and their peers want to hear when it comes to the prevention message. They want to hear all the facts communicated with realism, and respect for them as unique individuals. On another occasion, one young man came up to me after a drug education seminar and said, 'Hearing *all* the facts about drugs is going to make it easier to make the right decisions.'

So if young people do want to hear the right messages, what are the prevention measures you can take in your home and family environment to minimise the chances of your children abusing alcohol and drugs?

Prevention: build their self-esteem

More than fifteen years of involvement with addicts and alcoholics has taught me one fundamental lesson about the kind of person who is more likely to follow them down the same road. Basically, it's a person without any real self-esteem or a significant level of self-worth. It's someone who was never really loved and cherished as a unique and special individual. Therefore it follows that preventing your children from being controlled by drugs or alcohol is not about talking – it's about doing. It's primarily about building self-esteem and self-worth. So how do you do it?

- Let them know that you love them – demonstrate it, physically as well as verbally. In other words, don't just tell them, give them a hug.

- Respect them and treat them as unique individuals – for who they are rather than for what they can achieve.

- Respect their opinions by listening, and agreeing where appropriate.

- Show you are interested by spending 'quality time' with them, doing what they want to do as well as what you want to do.

- Reward the positive things they do, especially by telling them how much you appreciate their effort.

- Use words carefully, and remember how negative words can hurt.

- Help them to see that their asking for advice and help is something that brings *you* pleasure.

- Communicate with them regularly.

- Remember the following quote: 'I want to be loved and accepted totally apart from what I do. The fear of having to perform to be accepted dominates the thought life of most teenagers. All of us are driven to be accepted and loved. When we discover an unconditional love and acceptance with our parents, we are set free from trying to earn a dominating, emotionally draining performance-based love'.[4]

Prevention: practise what you preach

There is no point in telling our children that they need to avoid drinking too much, and to avoid drugs, if we do not maintain consistent standards ourselves.

1 Communicate your views about alcohol and drugs. For instance, this means telling your children how you control your drinking, and why you won't drink and drive. It means telling them why you don't take illegal drugs (or why you *do*!) and why you do/don't smoke. You also have to be open about why you take regular medication (if you do).

2 As regards alcohol use in the home, I would suggest you talk through with them your reasons for: (a) having drink permanently in the house, or not; (b) whether you personally will allow them to drink alcohol.

3 Discuss with them what principles they should adopt in connection with drinking alcohol away from home.

4 Proprietary medicines (e.g. painkillers) are often helpful, but what message do we give to children if we give them a tablet as soon as they ask for one? If they have a headache, maybe it would initially be better to tell them to lie down for half an hour. Then, if the headache doesn't go away, try *half* the advised dose to begin with.

5 Show a positive attitude to your health as well as theirs.

Prevention: be aware of the issues

Get to grips with the facts about drugs:

- Educate yourself about drugs by reading the appropriate parts of this book.

- If you talk to your children about drugs, be honest and realistic about all their effects, *including* the pleasant impact they might have.

- Take the opportunity to talk to your children about their views on drugs gleaned from the programmes, articles and reports they may have seen or read.

- Quietly and rationally, state alternative, realistic perspectives – but don't bully them! It is important, for instance, to tell them that while adverts for alcohol powerfully communicate the 'benefits', there is in fact a downside – such as hangovers, liver disease, making a fool of oneself in front of friends, etc.

- Don't patronise your children, and don't get angry if they refuse to see your point of view.

Prevention: help them to work out how they can say 'no'

The operative words here are 'help them'. *Telling* your children they *must* say 'no' is to ignore the pressure they are under in so many areas. It will also help if you preface any discussion by communicating that you are only too aware how difficult adolescence is for them, and that you want to understand them better. Having done this:

- Ask how they will say 'no' when they are offered a cigarette. Later you can talk about how they will say 'no' to other drugs such as alcohol and cannabis.

- Ask them how they cope with pressure from their friends on the subject of clothes, sex, etc. How are they going to say 'no' if they are offered drugs by their friends, if they can't cope with peer pressure over other things?

- Remind them of the fact that while 20 per cent of some groups do say 'yes' to drugs, *80 per cent* say 'no'.

- Very gently point out to them that the majority of addicts were first introduced to drugs by their friends.

Prevention: try to be friends with their friends!

Since most people are introduced to drugs by their friends, this is an important issue to consider further. This is a risky area, but it simply means being open and friendly to your son's or daughter's friends. It is also vital because, during adolescence, peer pressure is one of the most powerful forces in the universe. So in order to make things easier for your son or daughter and their friends:

- Make sure your children know they can invite their friends home.

- If their friends do come to your home, make sure they are welcome – even if you *don't* approve of their haircuts or clothes!

- Try to make contact with their friends' parents – always useful if there is a need to discuss issues like 'sleep-overs' and other party events.

- Never, ever criticise your children in front of their friends.

- If you have a problem with one of their friends, don't criticise them until you have asked your son or daughter something along the lines of 'Why does . . . do that sort of thing?'

Prevention: get involved with their school work and their school

In a major survey, which asked addicts and their families why they started taking drugs, one of the conclusions was that over 75 per cent of drug abusers were pressured by their parents to achieve good results at school.[5] These young people felt that their parents' love was conditional upon them achieving the right results. With this in mind, it is important to remember to:

1 Show that you are interested in their school work generally, and not just the marks or results they achieve.

2 Support the school by your involvement in activities.

3 Treat what the school says about your child and his/her abilities with caution, especially if it doesn't fit in with your perception. Assume your child is innocent, until proven (to your satisfaction) guilty.

4 Get to know your son's or daughter's teachers.

Prevention: check out the school's drug-prevention education and its policy on drug-takers

Most schools are developing drug-prevention education following recent government guidelines. Check it out to ensure that the lessons your children receive are balanced, for it is vitally important that they receive *all* the facts. Some drug educators in the past have actually told young people, 'Drug taking is only a phase you will go through.' The implications of this are that (a) you will use drugs, and (b) when it happens, you will come out the other end OK! It is also vital to ensure that both sides of the argument about legalisation are given equal weight, for otherwise your child may well assume that he or she is being told that drugs, and especially cannabis, are harmless.

You also need to check out how your child's school treats people who are found to be using drugs or pushing drugs. The vast majority of schools react in only one way: any involvement with drugs is met with expulsion. The problem is that this results in pushing the issue 'under the carpet' rather than using the circumstances as an opportunity to give a child, maybe your child, some valuable support and counselling.

All of this only goes to reinforce the point that when it comes to drugs, nothing is easy – especially the subject of prevention. Once again, I want to emphasise the fact that taking a caring, positive stance with your children is going to go a very, very long way towards convincing them that you love them enough to tackle all issues that may result in problems for them – and these, of course, include drugs and alcohol.

10 THINGS THAT HELP A CHILD BECOME A JUNKIE

1   Buying their love with money or things.

2   Demanding that they achieve.

3   Telling them they'll never measure up.

4   Not telling them that you love them.

5   Not showing them any physical affection.

6   Not talking to them, other than asking for something.

7   Not telling them that they are important, unique and special.

8   Putting them down in front of other people.

9   You and your partner not loving one another.

10 Putting possessions and work before them.

10 THINGS TO HELP ENSURE YOUR CHILD NEVER BECOMES A JUNKIE

1   Cherishing them as a unique individual, and telling them you are proud of them.

2   Telling them you accept them, both verbally and with hugs.

3   Teaching them that trying hard is important, but achievement is on their terms, not yours.

4   Trusting them.

5   Showing love and affection to your partner.

6   Talking with them – about them, and what they like.

7   Spending time with them.

8   Building them up in front of others.

9   LISTENING to them.

10   Telling them you love them.

4

Pills, Poppers and Caffeine

The whole subject of drugs is fraught with enormous debate and mythology. What do street nicknames like 'gear', 'smack', 'snow' and 'crack' mean? What effect does heroin have compared with LSD or ecstasy? Is it easier to withdraw from heroin or tobacco?

What follows answers these questions and other related issues. I will discuss each group of drugs in turn, in order to provide some important basic information about them; however, it is vitally important to remember the following points:

- The most important thing about addiction is not the drugs themselves, but the people concerned.

- You don't have to be an expert on drugs to help people.

- There is no such thing as a 'soft' drug.

- All addictive drugs affect the central nervous system in one way or another.

Legal drugs

I have included legal drugs for at least two reasons:

1 Millions more people are addicted to legal drugs such as alcohol, tobacco and tranquillisers than are addicted to illegal drugs.

2 Alcohol and tobacco each contribute far more to ill health and death than all the illegal drugs put together. It's predicted that

in the United Kingdom in 1995 alone, over 122,000 people will have died from smoking-related illnesses.

Bearing in mind that most children's first contact with drugs is at home or in a similar social setting, it's easy to see that parental example sets a very real trend for them. Therefore if youngsters do start to use legal or illegal drugs themselves, what objection can those parents who smoke or drink heavily really have?

Caffeine

The proliferation of coffee shops says a lot about the growing popularity of coffee. They cannot be looked upon as dens of drug iniquity: however, locked in the coffee they sell (unless it's decaffeinated) is a drug that affects the central nervous system. Its effect is low-key when taken in small quantities, but it is still a mild stimulant that increases alertness and can cause heartburn. What is clear, though, is that the consumption of coffee is growing very significantly. For instance, an article in *Hospital Doctor* describes how average use of this stimulant in the United States is now '500 mg of caffeine a day'.[1] This is the equivalent of five cups of coffee. (Certain other drinks contain significant quantities of caffeine as well: there are 41 mg in a cup of tea and 45 mg in a drink of Coca-Cola.)

The impact of caffeine at these levels is disturbing. It affects sleep, especially if taken just before going to bed. It influences our mood, and particularly our levels of anxiety and irritability. One study, reported in the *New England Journal of Medicine* (1986), confirmed that 'Men who drank five or more cups of coffee a day had an estimated relative risk for coronary heart disease of 2.49 compared with non-coffee drinkers.' So maybe there really is something to be said for keeping an eye on how many cups of coffee or tea we drink.

Tobacco

More than one heroin addict I've spoken to has stated, 'It has been much easier to quit heroin than tobacco.'

Why do people smoke?

The answers given to this question would probably be 'to relax' or 'to be sociable'. Smoking also, supposedly, reduces stress and tastes wonderful after sex or a good meal. The fact is, though, that once the habit is started, people who smoke carry on simply to get relief from their craving for nicotine.

What problems does smoking cause?

If you don't smoke, it's not just the smell of burning tobacco that is objectionable. Of far greater concern is the problem of passive smoking – that is, inhaling the smoke of other people's cigarettes. For those who are addicted to nicotine, the problems are far more serious. They include bronchitis, emphysema (leading to permanent damage to the lung tissue), heart disease and cancer.

On the bright side, though, it is an amazing fact that 11 million people in the UK gave up smoking between 1972 and 1988![2] Who said positive prevention doesn't work? But there is still a long, long way to go with something like 32 per cent of people over the age of sixteen still smoking.

Alcohol

The popularity and availability of alcohol today speaks volumes about why young people have a problem with our attitude towards other drugs. They read in the newspapers that 25,000 people a year die of alcohol-related illnesses, compared with about 400–500 people who die from all the illegal drugs put together.[3]

It is not only the vast quantities of alcohol that are consumed either – it's the lengths that the industry goes to in working overtime to tempt us to drink more. No wonder it's a £200 million business!

It is, of course, only legal to purchase alcohol if you are eighteen or over, and then only from licensed premises. It's said that over 90 per cent of us use alcohol as a normal social activity, and young people are catching on at a very early age. One survey concluded that 5 per cent of ten-year-old pupils are drinking *in excess of sensible adult limits*. The research involved 20,000 children (between fourteen and fifteen years old), and when asked what they did when they had a problem, 32.3 per cent of boys and 21.8 per cent of girls said that they had an alcoholic drink.[4] Little wonder, then, that people are saying that if alcohol had just been discovered, it would be banned – it would be made as illegal as heroin or 'crack'!

There can be very few people reading this book who have not experienced the effects of alcohol – even if only once. Contrary to popular assumption, alcohol is a depressant of the central nervous system – in spite of the way in which it can make people very voluble, excited and animated. On the downside, there are the hangovers, the lack of co-ordination (hence 'Don't Drink and Drive'), the lethargy, the irritability, the aggression and the violence. All in all, alcohol is physically and psychologically addictive, and can lead to untold despair and misery.

The Great Remover

It will remove stains from clothing. It will also
remove clothing from a man, a woman and children.
If used in sufficient quantity, alcohol will remove
furniture from the home, rugs from the floor, food
from the table, lining from the stomach, vision from
the eyes and judgment from the mind. Alcohol also
removes reputations, employment, friends, sanity,
freedom, happiness from children's hearts, people's
ability to adjust and live with others, and even life
itself.

AS A REMOVER OF THINGS, ALCOHOL HAS NO EQUAL

Solvents

Sally was thirteen and doing OK at school. She went around with a group of friends of about the same age, and one evening they were messing around at a friend's house while his parents were out. But it was rather boring, and one of the gang got a can of anti-perspirant and suggested that they each have a sniff to get high and have 'dreams'. Each member of the gang inhaled from the can, and some felt a strange effect, rather like being drunk.

When it was Sally's turn, she took a large breath. She became frightened by the effects. She ran up the stairs to go to the toilet to be sick, but collapsed on the landing. Fortunately, one of her friends had done a first-aid course, so he put her in the recovery position and cleared her airway, then gave her the kiss of life. The others called an ambulance.[5]

Sally's story ended happily – thanks to the doctors at her local hospital. Others are not so fortunate, though, and solvent abuse is growing. It is an activity that is difficult to control, with over thirty abusable, volatile substances in some households – including aerosol sprays, lighter fuel, solvent-based glues, dry-cleaning fluids, paint, thinners, correcting fluid and petrol. One government research paper has suggested that roughly 10 per cent of secondary-school pupils will try sniffing solvents at some time or other.

Why do people sniff solvents?

'It's easily available, gets you "drunk", and I can do it with my mates without anyone interfering.' Andrew is an ordinary lad from a good home, but he took some persuading to admit he does not like the feelings of being dizzy and 'spaced out' as a result of sniffing solvents.

What are the problems as a result of sniffing solvents?

Very real dangers involving solvents include damage to the heart, kidneys, liver, lung and brain, plus suffocation from:

1 Butane gas (which freezes the air passages when sprayed directly into the mouth).

2 Using plastic bags.

3 Choking on your own vomit if you pass out.

Tranquillisers

In 1992, there were over 16 million prescriptions for tranquillisers in the UK, but even that pales against the 1979 record of 30 million. There are hundreds of different types of tranquillisers, all of which are legally available on prescription. However, they become 'illegal' when stolen and sold for people to abuse.

The tranquillisers that are subject to misuse are mainly from the benzodiazepine family, and include Lorazepam (Ativan), Temazepam (Normison), Diazepam (Valium) and Nitrazepam (Mogadon). Street names include 'Moggies' and yellow or green 'eggs'.

Why are tranquillisers prescribed?

They are sometimes prescribed by doctors to help people cope during a crisis, because they reduce anxiety and stress or help people to sleep. In helping people to cope, however, they don't remove the problems – and sooner or later those problems have to be faced.

What are the problems associated with tranquillisers?

Tranquillisers not only decrease anxiety, but they also cause drowsiness, so that driving, using machinery or climbing a ladder, for instance, can be potentially dangerous. They are particularly hazardous when used with other sedatives and alcohol. The greatest concern about tranquillisers, however, relates to the fact that many people are prescribed them for very much longer than the recommended four- to six-week period. Addiction results, and withdrawal symptoms include severe irritability, anxiety, confusion and failure to cope with everyday activities.

Tranquillisers are possibly worse than any other drug

mentioned in this book, in that it can take weeks or even months to withdraw from them. However, it can be done by reducing the dosage by half a tablet a week or even a month. It is important to do this not only under medical supervision, but with the love and care of family, good friends and/or while belonging to a support group. John was eventually helped by a support group, but his story until then was truly disturbing:

> He was forty-one, and unemployed, and came off tranquillisers after a decade of addiction. He was originally prescribed Valium for anxiety following promotion. 'I felt under pressure,' he wrote, 'but it doesn't matter if you initially take tranquillisers for a sprained ankle through playing football, in the end they automatically give you mental problems. The mental feelings are like having a gin and tonic before going into a meeting – an artificial confidence. But they catch up with you and the side effects are very unpleasant – fear, panic, a pounding heart, sweating, headaches, shaking and insomnia. I used to travel the world, but when taking tranquillisers my reaction to a knock on the door was to crawl under the table. I was terrified.'[6]

Over-the-counter drugs (OTCs)

Many people are surprised that some medicines bought over the counter, such as cough mixtures and travel-sickness pills, can be used to obtain a 'buzz' or 'high'. It's for this reason that care needs to be taken to keep your home medicine cabinet locked. Drugs that can be misused include Gee's Linctus, Benylin and Sudafed. Many of them contain opioid drugs, such as codeine, or mild stimulants such as ephedrine. Alcohol is also a common ingredient of such medicines.

Lesser-known drugs

Amyl Nitrite (poppers, TNT, liquid gold)

This is a recreational drug, used in particular to heighten sexual arousal. Like all drugs, it has its downside, causing blackouts, vomiting (or worse) if used by someone with low blood pressure or a heart problem.

Ketamine (Special K)
Originally used as a veterinary drug, ketamine is abused as a relaxant; it also causes hallucination. It has been found on the rave scene, and some users of it become very aggressive.

Khat
Khat has been part of the culture of Somalia, Ethiopia and particularly the Yemen. It is the leaves of a bush and is chewed until it breaks down into a green paste. Khat is a stimulant, but leaves the regular user 'in neutral' – so that he or she loses interest in everyday issues. It can result in the loss of sex drive, and is also said to cause oral cancer.

Illegal drugs

Cannabis

'I was chronically shy. I was the last person I know out of my generation to start on drugs. I was thirteen when I was smoking cannabis.' So wrote Denholm Elliot's daughter Jennifer, in a recent newspaper article. She continued: 'The point is that you can't predict how you will react, even with cannabis. No one could have known how I was going to turn out after smoking a few joints. But you become tolerant to it. After I started smoking pot, I got into everything.'

Cannabis (also known as pot, grass, wacky backy, hash, weed, shit, dope or blow) is the most commonly used illegal drug in our society, and is now a readily acceptable part of social life, especially among young people. The easy availability of 'pot' is amazing, no doubt accelerated by the fact that most police forces will no longer charge anyone with its possession on the first occasion. Add to this the fact that a great many young people are being conned by the 'cannabis is safer than alcohol' brigade, and we have a recipe for disaster.

The facts about cannabis belie the myths, though. In comparison with alcohol, which is water-soluble, all sixty-one cannabinoids in the drug are only lipid- or fat-soluble. The consequence of this is that many of them remain in the body for far longer than alcohol does – up to four months, in fact. This 'hold-over' effect has been seen in pilots tested twenty-four hours after smoking just one ordinary-strength joint. They were unable to land their plane properly – fortunately, they were in flight simulators.[7]

It's also been confirmed that 'the tar content in a cannabis cigarette equals that of twelve tobacco cigarettes.'[8] In the proceedings of a 1992 symposium in Paris involving forty scientists from different countries, the plenary session concluded: 'The toxicity of cannabis is well established, experimentally and clinically. This drug adversely affects the central nervous system, the lungs, immunity and reproductive functions.' Such conclusions are further reinforced by over 10,500 accredited scientific papers collected by the University of Mississippi, not one of which gives cannabis a clean bill of health.

Why do people take cannabis?
The answer is because it makes them feel relaxed, talkative, gives them a sense of well-being, and makes some people giggle a lot.

What are the everyday problems associated with cannabis?
Impaired judgment is a fact of life when people use pot, which makes driving cars or other complicated tasks something of a risky business – not only for them, but for other people. Some cannabis-users experience profound and very disturbing anxiety attacks or hallucinations.

One nineteen-year-old sat in my office and made another point: 'Pot changed my attitudes. I used to try and forget my troubles, but they were still there and twice as bad in the morning. I also did not care what time I got up in the morning or whether I went to work or not.' In addition to this psychological dependence, smoking pot causes bronchitis and the risk of lung cancer is much greater than with tobacco smoking. Perhaps the problem that affects most cannabis-users is that it can be a 'gateway' drug to other dangerous drugs. This is because:

1 Having experienced instant gratification, they then want an even bigger 'buzz'.

2 Wherever you buy cannabis, there are often other drugs available – or, as one person put it, 'It's like going to get a packet of biscuits and ending up buying other things in the supermarket.'

Ecstasy

Ecstasy use is extremely widespread, and over 20 per cent of adults in one survey in Scotland stated that they took ecstasy frequently.[9]

Why do people use ecstasy?
One reason is that it can produce a calming effect that dissipates anger and hostility. At the same time, it gives a heightened perception of colour and sound, and increased energy and euphoria – no wonder it is used at raves! It is sold in tablet form (white, yellow or brown) and goes under one or other of these names – white doves, disco burgers, Adams, New Yorkers, XTC, fantasy, 'E'.

What problems are normally involved with ecstasy?
The list includes anxiety, confusion attacks, temporary paranoia, heightened sex drive, insomnia and depression, plus dehydration and exhaustion when used at raves. The other thing about it, which crops up with so many drugs, is co-ordination problems – thus making driving and the use of machinery particularly dangerous. Ecstasy also lowers inhibitions – which has implications for exploitation, sexual contact and HIV transmission.

Dangers of using ecstasy

Because it is a stimulant, ecstasy can be dangerous if you have a heart problem or high blood pressure, or a tendency to epileptic fits or mental illness. An article in *Blitz* magazine described a worrying and growing situation:

> Ecstasy casualties have rocked clubland. Weekend E-heads have complained of depression and paranoia after withdrawal. On the street, Tom is a young entrepreneurial type, a wideboy at the warehouse raves who now works in the City. 'People ask you for things, you ask for things, you know what I mean?'
>
> He took E a few years ago when it was considerably more pure. 'These days with the competition, everyone trying to sell E, you don't know what you're getting.' He has personally avoided the smack-Es, but has observed the result. 'You don't want to dance. You don't want to talk. You're in your own little world.'

Amphetamines

Amphetamines have been around a long time; they were once sold as nasal decongestants. They were also given to troops in the Second World War to keep them awake in combat. Known in the 1960s as Purple Hearts, amphetamines (or speed, uppers, whizz, ice) are the most commonly used stimulants, although experts expect 'crack' to take over in the not too distant future.

Speed is normally sold as an off-white crystallised powder, and is usually 'snorted' through the nose, or injected by more serious users.

Why do people use amphetamines?

To keep awake to enjoy themselves, to party, to give them confidence and seemingly endless energy.

What are the common problems and dangers associated with amphetamines?

They cause strong mood swings coupled with paranoia, or even major mental disorder (psychosis). You itch and/or lose your appetite, which is why they were once used as slimming pills. Users quickly develop a tolerance, and need more and more speed to get the same effect. Feelings of acute anxiety may also exist, sometimes even years after users have stopped taking the drug.

There are further dangers associated with speed if a user has a heart problem or an existing psychological disorder.

Cocaine and crack

Cocaine (also known as coke and snow) is often described as the 'champagne' drug because it was used in the City, while crack is associated with inner-city poverty and deprivation. Yet the fact that the 'impact' or 'rush' of crack is infinitely greater than that of cocaine means that it is used right across the class barriers. Both cocaine and crack are expensive compared with other drugs.

Crack (known as rocks) is cocaine converted into a very pure form in which it can be smoked instead of injected, sniffed or swallowed. This drug carries with it a growing reputation for its impact on users, which has been described in the following way:

The difference between snorting cocaine and smoking it is like the difference between firing an air gun and a mortar. The user sets off on a steady downward spiral towards a state of depression and paranoia, as intense and agonising as the drug's high was euphoric. It is while sliding towards that state, desperate for more crack, consumed by the paranoid's angry view of the world enveloping him or her, that abusers are at their most dangerous. In that cycle, abusers can and frequently do explode into wild, irrational behaviour, violence and criminality. One of the legends of the New York Police Department's narcotics division is of a youth in a crack-induced state of paranoia who sliced off his grandmother's head with a kitchen knife, then went strolling through the neighbourhood carrying it by the hair as though it was a sack of groceries. Crack has been described as a marketing miracle. It might have been, but it was no accident. It was rather the consequence of a well-calculated strategy by the drug barons in the South American country of Colombia, the centre of the world's cocaine trade, using the same marketing acumen Procter & Gamble devotes to bringing a new soap powder to the marketplace.[10]

Why are crack and cocaine used?
Because they have a rapid stimulant effect, bringing with it alertness and aggressive confidence.

What are the problems?
One drug-rehabilitation worker put it this way: 'Heroin users can go on for twelve years without losing their mental stability, but crack can provoke a crisis within two to three years because of the powerful effects of the drug.'

Other problems, particularly related to smoking crack, include shortness of breath and even severe chest pains. Also, there is depression, nose ulcers, sleeplessness, weight loss, convulsions, paranoid psychosis, as well as all the problems such as HIV and hepatitis B infection that are associated with intravenous injection of any drug.

Hallucinogens

Two of the most commonly used hallucinogens are LSD (acid, tabs, tripe) and Liberty Cap mushrooms (mushies, magic mushrooms or shrooms):

LSD (lysergic acid diethylamide) Illegal. Sold in minute quantities – often on sugar cubes or on small squares of printed blotting paper – that are then put on the tongue.

Liberty Cap mushrooms Legal if they are eaten raw, but you could be charged with a criminal offence if you prepared them by drying or cooking them.

Why are LSD and magic mushrooms used?

These substances are not addictive in the same sense as other drugs, but users are drawn back to them to experience the hallucinatory 'trips'. In fact, various perceptual disturbances are more common than the hallucinations, e.g. distortion of colours, sight and sounds.

The effect on the mind, however, is very dependent on the mental state you are in at the time you use the drug. The environment you are in also plays a part in the experience you enjoy or, alternatively, hate. Talkativeness or giggling incessantly are common results.

What problems are associated with hallucinogens?

Flashbacks of 'trips' can be experienced many months after you had the last one. However, confusion, lethargy, depression and disorientation are more common experiences. Occasionally, serious or even fatal injuries are sustained as a result of acting on hallucinatory experiences, e.g. thinking you can fly!

Heroin

Once assumed to be the drug of the 'loser', the person who had been through the chains of all the other drugs, heroin today can be the first drug of choice after alcohol or tobacco for some young people. It is also used in partnership with other drugs. Crack-users, for instance, use it to minimise the dreadful depression that comes on every time they use crack.

Heroin (also known as H, junk, smack, horse, skag) is derived from the opium poppy. It invariably comes in the form of a greyish, brownish powder. It is injected, having been heated on a spoon with some water. Most people today, however, begin using heroin by 'chasing the dragon', which is sniffing the smoke from heroin heated on tin foil.

There are some forms of synthetic opioid, such as methadone, which are used as a means of helping heroin addicts. Methadone is used either to help them withdraw from heroin, or – increasingly – to maintain addiction without the supposed need to buy heroin on the black market. Sadly, the majority of addicts will tell you it is very much more difficult to withdraw from methadone than from heroin.

Why do people use heroin?
Because they enjoy the almost immediate sense of warmth, and because it makes pain or problems seem more tolerable.

What are the common problems and dangers involved in heroin use?
Addiction to heroin develops very quickly. Some very basic problems are constipation, nausea, vomiting and abscesses. Withdrawal is very uncomfortable (although rarely as bad as portrayed in the media), and may be equated to extremely bad flu coupled with stomach cramp and insomnia. It lasts anything from seven to fourteen days.

If you are injecting opioids, there is, of course, the danger of HIV, AIDS and hepatitis, and it is also vital to be aware of the great danger of overdosing.

5

The Nightmare Scenario

Facing up to the fact that your child or partner may be using drugs will be a profoundly difficult time for you. Of course, the facts may eventually prove your suspicions to be unfounded. However, if your worst fears are confirmed, I can assure you that there is hope, real hope. With lots of love, and especially 'tough' love, many people do break free from drugs.

How can I tell if my child is using drugs?

One mother describes what she felt was a terrible discovery but which was actually of very great importance:

Five weeks ago, I found some cannabis tucked into my sixteen-year-old son's bedroom drawer as I was putting away his clean clothes. Then, further down, in among a secret stash of 'Page Three' pictures, there was a tiny, very tiny, packet of white powder: cocaine. Over the past eighteen months, Jack had become so arrogant and difficult that he was almost unbearable. He was moody, frequently exhausted, yet couldn't sleep. Often I would hear him moving about the house at night. I had asked him, as tactfully as I could, if he was taking drugs, and was dismissed with outbursts of anger. Over the summer, I even discreetly examined his tanned arms for needle marks, feeling faintly ludicrous.[1]

The facts for this mother were clear-cut, but for many people the evidence is not as conclusive. It is so very difficult to be absolutely sure that your child is actually using drugs for one very significant reason – most of the evidence relates to the 'normal' behaviour of adolescent development. Yet, while acknowledging this fact, there are still 'pointers' which are often obvious over a period of time if someone is abusing drugs.

Emotional signs of drug abuse

Teenagers go through some pretty wild mood swings in the space of only twenty-four hours, let alone over several months. However, drug abuse can result in:

- Changes in personality that could relate to the particular drug they are using. Stimulants will make them hyperactive, so that they are restless not only in the day but also at night. Hallucinogens, e.g. LSD, can cause some people to become paranoid, so that they feel that everyone is out to make life as difficult as possible for them. Depressants will make them very sleepy, and possibly cause them to have slurred speech.

- Radical mood swings, which can include excessive irritation, outbursts of anger and restlessness.

- Being over-tired for no real reason.

Physical signs of drug abuse

Yet again, dramatic changes in appearance are often the norm during adolescence, but drug abuse may clearly be involved if there are:

- Very erratic eating habits.

- Dilated or constricted pupils of the eyes.

- Red blotchiness around the mouth and nose.

- *Excessive* acne. (Don't get over-suspicious about this one, please, without a lot more clues. I mean, how do you identify zits on top of zits?)

- Irregularity of periods.

External indicators relating to drug abuse

These factors *may* be indicative of someone who is abusing drugs or alcohol:

- Disappearance of clothes or other personal effects, especially *your* clothes and personal effects.

- Pocket money or allowance gets used up very, very quickly (i.e. within the first day), or there is evidence of heavy borrowing.

- Hanging out in strange places, especially at school (e.g. behind the bicycle shed).

- Increasingly erratic attendance at school and/or no interest in getting work done.

- Very limited attention span.

- Excessive interest in highly paid jobs.

- Poor attendance at normal workplace.

- Involvement with old friends is gradually (or quickly) replaced by a new group of associates.

- Different vocabulary.

- Loss of interest in long-established hobbies.

- Wearing sunglasses (to hide constricted or dilated pupils).

- Radical changes in style of clothes or jewellery.

- Smell of glue on clothes.

- Heavy use of aftershave or perfume to hide smell of glue or alcohol.

- New yearning for peppermint – this can indicate that smoking is an issue.

- 'Strange' smells in bedroom, and/or bedroom window kept wide open for long periods of time.

- Appearance and disappearance of new clothes or other goods, indicating shoplifting.

- Secretive phone calls, especially from people who don't know your child well.

- Avoiding family contact.

Specific evidence of drug use

This is dealt with in more detail in Chapter 4, but evidence would include:

- Remains of cigarette ends or 'joints'.

- Strong, sweet, aromatic, smoky smells.

- 'Strange-looking' tobacco.

- Pills or powders.

- Needles and/or syringes.

- Blackened foil or spoons.

- Small squares of blotting paper with futuristic designs.

Like you, I hope you never ever find anything more shocking than the fact your fifteen-year-old has thrown Eric the teddy bear in the dustbin! But, if you do, there are still ways in which you can minimise the potential damage in many areas. After all, alienation of your child is the last thing that is needed if you are to help them break free of their possible drug abuse.

Keeping a sense of proportion

Individual responses to finding out that a child is abusing drugs or alcohol are rarely what we think they would be. Faced with the evidence, many parents who imagined they would be frantic have been amazingly calm. With others, it has been completely the opposite, and frenzy has been the result. Of course, there are some who react with studied indifference on the basis that they use drugs themselves and do not consider it a problem! Anger, however, usually erupts sooner or later, along with a whole range of other emotions, questions and responses, including:

- Personal recrimination – spending hours going over personal failures.

- The 'scapegoat' routine – whose fault is it really?

- How could this possibly happen to me?

- What is going to happen to my child?

- Coping with the humiliation.

- Working out what to tell and who to tell.

- Feelings of brokenness, pain and failure.

- A deep sense of inadequacy.

- Struggling to cope with everyday routines.

- Desperately wanting to share, but overwhelmed by the shame.

- An overpowering compulsion to deny what you know to be true.

- Feeling desperately disappointed in, and let down by, your child.

- Sensing a lack of control over your child.

Finally, there is the heartbreak of betrayal and the strong belief that everything you have ever done has been a complete waste of time.

Initial responses

Probably the strongest compulsion that most people have is to
shut the problem out and just hope that it will go away. Others
react by sitting the abuser down, telling them what's wrong,
telling them how to put it right, and then assuming the problem
has been dealt with.

Anyone who has 'been there' will tell you that neither of these
options work. There are, however, some basic rules that will help
to ensure that your relationship is maintained – and perhaps even
improved – before getting down to dealing with the situation.
What happens at this point is going to make a fundamental
difference to the next six months to two years.

- **Don't lash out:** at anyone, but especially the person who is
  abusing. Do everything possible to keep talking to them as
  constructively as possible. If you can't respond positively, say
  nothing; but if you have to say something, think seriously
  about writing something down and handing it to them later.
  Either way, try to convince them that – despite their actions –
  you still love them as your child or partner.

- **Face the truth about yourself:** do not deny the situation
  or what it is costing you. Do not be tempted to look too
  far into the future; if you do, you will probably feel overwhelmed. If it's at all possible, share your thoughts about the
  situation with someone especially about how *you* feel. If you
  don't have someone close to talk to, then go to your doctor,
  your church minister, the Samaritans or one of the major
  organisations listed in the Resources section at the end of this
  book.

  Being forced to acknowledge personal failure is incredibly
  difficult for anyone, but facing the truth about ourselves really
  does give us the liberty to help others more effectively.
  Actually acknowledging our own vulnerability can be tremendously liberating to others, especially the person with the drug
  problem.

- **Face the truth about the time needed to sort the issues out:** we live in an age of instant gratification, instant answers and trite sound-bites. The fact is that there are no quick answers to the problem of a person abusing drugs or alcohol. The issues are invariably complex, and it is going to take a lot of time to sort out attitudes and patterns of behaviour that have become deeply rooted. Breaking free is going to be incredibly time-consuming – especially for you.

- **Remember that there are other people in the family:** others who need your love, acceptance and time. They are just as important as the person who is abusing drugs, and it's worth making the decision to cope, even if it's just for them. They are especially important if most of your time does get taken up in helping the family member with the drug problem. You cannot split yourself in two, but you can tell the other family members, as often as possible, that you love them, that they are still vitally important to your life, as well as ensuring that you spend time with them.

Practical steps to help

The list of things you can do to help someone in the family is extensive, but remember to take one step at a time.

Establish if they really want help

It may be that they don't think they have a problem or, even if they do, that they don't want your help – yet. If they do not want help, remember that there are plenty of other things you can do to build for the future.

Keep channels of communication open

Whatever happens, do not compromise on this one – stay in touch, in so far as it is down to you. Keep talking, even if they don't want to stop using drugs. One day they *will* want to make changes, and they will need to be able to talk to you when that time comes.

Listen

While it is easier to talk than to listen, really work at listening. It may be that you are the first person for many years who is willing to take the time to listen to them. Remember that really *communicating that you are listening* requires effort:

- Make eye contact, so that the person *knows* you are interested.

- Don't butt in – wait until they want to hear your viewpoint.

- Work hard at hearing what they are really saying, and not what you *think* they are saying.

Be vulnerable

Acknowledge your own mistakes, and accept responsibility for your part in who and what they are. You haven't got a lot to lose, but you do have everything to gain. Tell them how you used to feel with your parents; how you rebelled; what you really feel about issues; why you behave in the way that you do.

Tell them you are sorry

Very, very few people have ever done that to them before. Other people have been too insecure to tell them they are sorry. Telling them you are really sorry for what you have done wrong will do more to communicate your real love for them than many other things that you do.

Learn to trust them

It is difficult to learn to trust someone who has betrayed you and caused you hurt and pain. This is especially true of drug addicts or alcoholics who, in order to buy their next fix or drink, will often manipulate and con anyone they can. However, it is important that they hear you say, 'I will take what you say to me as being true about you personally, but when it comes to what you say about other people or your physical needs, I reserve the right to get further evidence.' It all sounds a little formal, but the principle behind it is important, so say it the best way you can.

Don't allow yourself to be conned and manipulated

Don't give or lend money, because it may be used for drugs or alcohol. If the person concerned needs something, then buy the article itself – e.g. food or clothing.

Be firm and set out the rules

Set out some rules, and fairly and consistently maintain them until you believe that it's the right time to change them. Do not allow them to do things which are unacceptable to you and the other people in your family, e.g. using drugs in the home. Similarly, refuse to do anything that may support their drug use, e.g. buying them drugs or alcohol. Reinforce the standards you want in your home if they want it to be their home as well.

Don't allow them to use unacceptable or obscene language or vulgar behaviour. Tell them you don't want them to be dirty and smelly, and insist that they take a bath or shower.

Take time out for yourself

Coping with someone who is abusing drugs or alcohol is physically, mentally and emotionally draining; so at some point each week, make some time for yourself.

Get support for yourself

There are many groups of people who will provide an opportunity for you to recharge your emotional and spiritual batteries, and who will understand what you are going through. Many

people in churches, synagogues and other places of worship are
no strangers to problems – try them. Self-help groups for those
in the same situation as you can also be very, very helpful. There
are national addresses and telephone numbers at the back of this
book so that you can find out details of resources close to your
home. One woman wrote about the difference this made to both
her and her husband:

> We took ourselves off to meetings of Family Anonymous. I
> felt guilty because I thought it was all my fault. I was working
> full-time and had not spent enough time with my two sons.
> My sponsor there was quite the opposite. She had stayed at
> home and had devoted herself to her children, and yet she had
> a child using drugs.
>
> You can't imagine how reassuring it was to discover that it
> wasn't all our fault.
>
> Richard and I ditched our social life, and for about four
> months we went to five meetings a week in an effort to get
> some sense back into our lives.

What to do in emergencies

What follows is all about how to face up to the issues of calling
the police, detecting a overdose and dealing with medical emer-
gencies. Before I offer some guidelines, I would strongly emphasise, on the strength of my personal experience with many
hardened addicts, that drug-users are far more aware of the issues
involved than they would have you believe. What I mean by this
is that they always know, before you do, when they have crossed
an unacceptable line. They know when they are pushing the
limits, and they know – even if they won't admit it – that you are
justified in taking the action you need to take. No addict, no
matter what drugs they are on, has lost sight completely of what
is right and wrong. Do your best, but when it comes to the point
where other people's lives take priority over the drug-abuser's
actions, then act decisively.

When to involve the police

If you even have to think of involving the police, then the situation has become very serious. The need to do so is invariably related to the following.

1 Drug use at home

If you have rightly made it very clear that using drugs at home is unacceptable, but your child continues to do so when you have asked them to stop, then you may have to call the police. If you do, then don't make a major issue out of it; instead, very calmly make it clear that if they use drugs in the home one more time, you will very definitely phone the police or go to the police station to ask their advice. Having said this, you must then do it if those circumstances arise.

2 When your life or someone else's life is threatened

There is very little point in debating this one. You simply have to accept that *no one* has the right to threaten anyone's life, whether they are an addict or not.

3 When you and other people are being 'ripped off'

Stealing from their own family means that the person doing it has reached the stage where you have no option but to involve the police. Simply warn them that if they steal or con anyone known to you personally, then you will advise the police. Again, having said this, you must remain true to your word.

Medical emergencies

If, as a result of drug use, a person is becoming disruptive (usually alcohol or tranquillisers have this effect), you need to take them somewhere quiet and dimly lit, and persuade them to sit down. If they want to lie down or if they fall asleep, put them in the recovery position which means laying them on their stomach with their face to one side. Stay with them if at all possible, but if you have no choice but to leave them, then check them every fifteen minutes to ensure that they have not become unconscious (see 'Typical features of an overdose' below). When dealing with people who are experiencing acute medical problems after taking drugs, it is *vital* to try to determine the following information:

1 Is the person an experienced user?

2 What did they take (or what did they think they took)? If they have friends with them, check with them what it was; it might be that they know something that the user doesn't.

3 Ask how much they took (again, enlist the help of friends in confirming this).

4 How did they take it? It is much more common to overdose by injecting or swallowing than by smoking.

5 **MOST IMPORTANT** – *Was the drug taken in combination with alcohol or while the person was under the influence of alcohol?* Alcohol is extremely dangerous when mixed with drugs. In many overdose fatalities the actual quantity of a drug consumed might be minimal, but the addition of alcohol can make it a lethal combination.

Typical features of an overdose

1 Friends start to express concern.

2 The person has taken more than one drug. Alcohol is particularly dangerous when combined with 'downers' (e.g. tranquillisers, heroin, DF118 – a painkiller – or barbiturates).

3 There is slurred speech, drooping eyelids or they are staggering around.

4 If they have used stimulants, they will have very *dilated* (large) pupils. Following opiate use, pupils are very *constricted* (small).

5 They are unconscious. The way to establish whether someone is deeply unconscious rather than asleep is to give them a 'Chinese burn': pinch their earlobes hard or, as a last resort,

rub your knuckles very hard up and down their sternum (breastbone) or (even more painful) to one side of their sternum.

WHENEVER SOMEONE IS UNCONSCIOUS, IT IS ESSENTIAL THAT YOU GET THEM INTO THE RECOVERY POSITION (lay them on their stomach with their face to one side), SO THAT THEY DO NOT CHOKE ON THEIR OWN VOMIT. IF SOMEONE DOES BECOME UNCONSCIOUS, DON'T MESS ABOUT. SEND FOR MEDICAL OR FIRST-AID HELP IMMEDIATELY, ENSURING THAT SOMEONE REMAINS WITH THE PATIENT AT ALL TIMES. ENLIST THE HELP OF FRIENDS IF NECESSARY.

If when checking with others what drugs have been used you don't understand the jargon or slang, then ask them for the medical name for the drug. Pass this information on to the ambulance crew, doctor, hospital – whoever it is that is helping.

If you have to call an ambulance

Do not agonise about whether to tell the hospital what the real problem is – not to do so may cost the person their life. If you find the user unconscious and have to get them to hospital, take with you, or give to the ambulance crew, any packets, syringes (handle very carefully and put in a can or box) or even samples of vomit. This is not pleasant, but it may save the person's life.

6

The Family – Working Towards Freedom

Creating a family environment in which real change can take place in the life of a drug-abuser or alcoholic is never easy, but it is possible. Amid all the problems, aggravation, pressure and stress, one can take steps that will build a resource of real love and hope for the future. I say that change is possible with confidence, because I've lived and worked with my own family in such an environment for many years at Yeldall Manor. Here we have tried and tested principles in a community of twenty-five addicts and alcoholics who wanted to sort their lives out. Those principles are not perfect, but they have brought about the changes that you long to see in the life of the person with an addiction problem in your family.

Love and acceptance

One of the most amazing things about Yeldall Manor that people comment on is the feeling of peace that they sense in the place, in the lives of both the residents and staff. Some of their surprise must be down to what they think a rehabilitation centre is like. They come expecting to find a building full of 'junkies' and 'alcoholics', all either shaking from withdrawal or shuffling around almost brain-dead. Instead, they find a group of relatively happy staff and residents, seeking to love and accept one another – *most* of the time, at least! The confirmation that love and acceptance does actually work is founded on the evidence of many, many changed lives.

'Tough' love

'Tough' love is selfless, unconditional love that is prepared to say 'no'. It's love that goes on caring for people as well as taking the pain of their hurt and anguish. This type of love is necessary at Yeldall Manor and in your home, because it is not the physical addiction that is the hardest thing for addicts to face, but:

1 Dismantling the psychological addiction – in other words, changing the mind-set and attitudes that have been built up over the years.

2 Choosing to face, without drugs or alcohol, the full impact of painful feelings and emotions that have been cushioned by the drugs or alcohol, sometimes for over twenty years.

3 Having to face, without drugs or alcohol, the hurt and pain they have caused other people – and especially those closest to them.

Every staff member at Yeldall Manor will readily confirm that unconditional, selfless love is not easily come by. I had only been at Yeldall for about three months when I decided that I had had enough; I discovered that any love I arrived with had already been used up. I remember praying to God, 'I can't love these people any more. They've taken what I've given them and it hasn't brought the results I expected. There's no way I can do this job any more.' In response to my prayer, I felt as if God was telling me to be a channel for *his* unlimited love, rather than struggling to help the addicts with my own strength.

I can't pretend to you that I always responded well after that – and, besides, there are too many residents and staff who will tell you otherwise. What I do know is that it gradually got easier, because I was dependent no longer on my own love but instead on the bottomless reservoirs of God's love.

Acceptance

People with drug or alcohol problems have spent many years building a false foundation, creating in their minds the perfect person that they think will impress other people. They also act in a way that they think will cause you and me to treat them in a special manner, and this makes them feel worthy. In order to redress these major problems, addicts need genuine acceptance, so that over the months they can begin to face up to who they really are and allow others to know them as they really are. Yet how do you accept them? The answer is by looking behind the image, the anger, the bitterness and the rebellion, and looking instead for the very special person they were created to be.

Facing up to reality

I suggest that you take some time, albeit through gritted teeth, to try to get yourself into the frame of mind where you can begin to love and accept the addicted person for his or her own sake, rather than demanding changes for your sake.

Wanting immediate results is understandable, but not very realistic because it only reinforces differences between you and them. There are practical steps to take, but before we look at them, can I also suggest that you find someone to help *you* to face up to the issues involved? Hopefully, it will be your partner; but if you don't have one, or they can't get beyond the raw emotions stage, then look for someone else.

Before we look at a list of practicalities, one final thing. Get everyone else in the immediate family together and face the situation for what it is, honestly and openly. It's also important to have regular meetings after that to talk through what is happening and who is saying what. I've found that daily staff meetings at Yeldall Manor make a big difference in many areas, but especially in preventing the residents from manipulating us by playing one staff member off against another. These meetings are not gossip sessions – they are far too serious for that, because people's lives depend on them – but they are an opportunity to share information about how a resident is progressing. Anything really confidential is shared only with the resident's regular counsellor. Regular meetings also help if there is something that is going wrong, especially when it involves more than one member of the family, because you can then face the issue together.

Practical steps – love in action

Facing the facts

Assuming that the evidence you have got really does confirm your family member is abusing drugs or alcohol, then prepare yourself to talk through with them what you have learnt.

- Prepare the time and place very carefully. Don't do it just before they are going out, because, on top of the frustration of your confrontation, they will get wound up by the fact that you are preventing them from meeting friends. Pick a time when you all have space, even if it means waiting a while. Be prepared to take time off work if necessary.

- Be realistic; accept that your approach will be seen as confrontation, so don't make it worse by behaving angrily or arrogantly. You might be wrong in your suppositions; but if you *are* right, remember that they have been preparing for this moment longer than you have. They have probably been rehearsing for many months their response to your accusation and your indignation. They have also got all their answers and excuses ready, and will almost certainly deny the truth.

- Remember that if they are using drugs or alcohol, then because you now know for certain, they will believe that their world is about to fall apart. They will feel that you are threatening their whole security, friends, lifestyle and standards. Maybe more vital than that, they will believe that they may be forced to stop abusing the drugs or alcohol that they now depend upon for their very stability to cope with everyday life.

What steps you take from this point are dependent upon whether or not they acknowledge that they have a problem.

If they deny they are abusing drugs or alcohol

You have little option but to take their denial at face value – don't beat about the bush. Explain (preferably calmly) the evidence, and ask them to state why that evidence is invalid. If they still deny abusing drugs, all you can do is to tell them that you will aim to carry on as if nothing has happened. Ask them to understand, however, that you would not have gone through the pain of confronting them if you had not thought about it long and hard. Reinforce the fact that you love them (and go on showing your love in practical ways), but that you reserve the right to question their behaviour in the future. Keep your guard up while still seeking to love them and respect them.

If they acknowledge they are abusing drugs or alcohol

In this situation, try to remain calm and to establish whether or not they want to do something about stopping. Once they have told you their answer, try not respond immediately, so you can give yourself time to think. Tell them you will arrange to meet them again so that you can talk through what should happen in the future. However, if it's clear that they want help, then start looking at what options are available, and who they can get advice from.

If they don't want to stop abusing drugs or alcohol

You will need to take time to think through the following issues.

1 What drug or alcohol use, if any, is acceptable in your home?

2 Is it still appropriate for them to see all their friends?

3 Should they continue to receive the same financial allowance?

4 Should they still be allowed to use the family vehicle?

5 What 'free time' are they allowed outside the home?

6 Should they continue to live at home? If you don't believe it's appropriate for them to leave immediately, then they should know that you retain this option as a possibility for the future. Remaining at home will be dependent upon their willingness to respect the rest of the family.

It is difficult to be specific in any of these areas; and it may be that, having made one decision, circumstances result in you being more or less rigid subsequently. Once again, taking your time is important in order to build relationships and seek advice.

If they do want to give up abusing

Given a positive response, it is important to reach *agreement* as to the best ways of helping them to stop using drugs or alcohol. Only time will tell if they are really serious about giving up. One very rough guide as to their seriousness is the way they respond to restrictions, but remember to apply those restrictions with the right attitude. Before going too far down this road, take some of the following practical steps:

- Talk with experts, e.g. doctors and drug agencies.

- Try really hard to listen before you react.

- Don't discuss issues if the person is 'stoned' or drunk.

- Don't discuss or argue if they patently don't want to listen. All this does is reinforce in their minds that it's:

  you who is being unreasonable.

you who does not know the 'real' story.
you who needs to change.

- Keep seeking the truth by establishing the facts rather than responding to emotion.

- Plan when you will regularly meet with them, and ensure that *you* stick to the arrangement. If you really have to change the meeting time, then do it very rarely and only with the other person's agreement.

- Invest your time in them – how else do they know how important they are to you?

- It may be helpful or appropriate to involve someone else as a mediator, someone whom you can both trust. This will go a long way towards defusing potentially difficult situations.

- Don't meet to discuss issues for too long – their attention span is, as with everyone with an addiction problem, very limited.

- Keep asking 'Why?' but *nicely*:

  'David, why did you take drugs?'
  '*Well, because they felt good.*'
  'In what way did they feel good?'
  '*They made me feel comfortable.*'
  'Why did you feel the need of comfort from them?'

- Constantly reinforce the fact that while you love them, you don't love their behaviour or attitude.

- Accept responsibility for your actions.

- Be prepared to say sorry.

- Tell them you will not do *anything* that reinforces their drug-taking.

- Keep your word. If they can't trust *you*, who can they trust, and why should they change?

- Stand by them in any action they have to take, e.g. court appearances. But don't protect them from the consequences of their actions.

- Don't be afraid of physical contact, even if they shrug off a hand on the arm or shoulder.

- Keep on checking whose insecurities you are responding to – yours or theirs?

- Remember that they are afraid of failure just as much as you are.

- Check to ensure that they think the change agreed is reasonable, e.g. is it really practical for them to give up smoking tobacco while they are in the middle of studying for exams?

- Tell them how well they have done when they do make positive changes.

- Play to their strengths.

- Be very careful how much money you trust them with. If necessary, you can always buy them the things that they really need.

- Finally, don't agree to unreasonable demands; keep your options open, e.g. when they ask, 'Please don't tell Gran and Grandpa, will you?' Think through your response carefully: 'No, I can't honestly agree not to tell them at all, but I am prepared to keep it from them for the moment. You must remember that they need protecting as much as you do.'

Remember the rest of the family
Other members of the family need the reassurance that they are loved when you make a major investment of your time in the person with the problem. So try to work out some special times for them. Tell them that you love them – and show it!

Remember you can't do it for them

Another hard lesson we learn at Yeldall Manor is that we can't change addicts. They have to make the choice for themselves that they want to be free of their addiction, and until they do this nothing much happens. Worst of all, you may have to let them fall even further into the mire. If you do try to stop them, then I am afraid it will take longer for them to come face to face with reality – and with the truth about themselves. Leaving them to fall will cause you great anguish and distress, but it will result in them freeing themselves from their addiction sooner.

I realise that all this is easy for me to say, but that it's a member of *your* family I am talking about. All I can do is reinforce what I have learned: that there never has been an addict or alcoholic who *wanted* to be an addict or alcoholic. They long for freedom more than you will ever know, but the distance between where they are and the freedom they cry out for, on the inside, is huge. As you love them and give them the dignity of treating them as responsible individuals, they will slowly and falteringly take the steps that lead to that real freedom.

7

Family Life and the Addict

Helping people with a life-dominating problem is demanding (yet fulfilling) work, and one of the most exciting things about working with addicts and alcoholics is learning to see the potential in their lives. It takes time, because their initial attitude is often one of unrestrained negativity. It shows itself in arrogance, rebellion, pain, bitterness and pure despair. As time goes by, though, you begin to understand what's behind the negativity. The root problems are not in fact drugs, or the attitudes that manifest themselves in words and actions. These things simply cover up the emptiness inside, the feelings of insecurity, inferiority and insignificance. Behind the anger, rebellion and bitterness, there is a person who is intelligent, sensitive, and longing to be loved and accepted. There is also a unique individual with the potential to contribute directly and positively to you, your family and society in general.

Helping an addict to find the freedom to become that unique individual is not easy. The necessary change can only take place in an environment where an addict is not only loved, but is also helped to face up to his or her life as it really is – the good, the bad and the ugly! We have created such an environment at Yeldall Manor; and though it's not perfect, it does enable addicts and alcoholics to find freedom in the fulfilment of serving others.

Yeldall Manor is not an easy place for residents to live, because it demands of them a lot of sacrifice, as well as the courage to face up to themselves as they really are, instead of the image they have hidden behind for a number of years. Many people find that

process much easier by finding faith in the forgiving and trans-
forming power of God's love in Jesus; however they do it,
though, it's critically important that they discover:

- **Security:** they need to find a sense of belonging, a sense of
  being loved and unconditionally accepted.

- **Significance:** they need to begin to enjoy a sense of purpose,
  meaning, adequacy and a sense of being able to contribute.

- **Self-worth:** they need to acquire a sense of being valued for
  who they really are.

Having these needs met is a painful experience for residents,
because it reinforces the fact that these are needs that could or
should have been met in their families. In fact, if you spend time
talking with residents about family life, some of the pain they
express makes you want to weep. Not long ago, I gave some of
the residents the opportunity to describe their most vivid recol-
lection of family life. Among their responses were the following:

'There wasn't really any structure to my family life.'
'Everyone did their own thing, and I wasn't even involved with
   what the others were doing.'
'I had no relationships in my family life that gave me security
   and love.'
'When my adopted father came home, I was discarded by my
   mother for fear my father would be jealous.'
'I was constantly told how much of an unwanted accident I
   was, about how useless, ugly and stupid I was, and how I
   would never amount to anything.'

These memories are painful enough, but are no match for the
true story of one resident who came home from school when he
was eight years old to be told, after hours of waiting outside an
empty house, that the rest of the family had moved out. He was
left behind *deliberately*, and yet somehow was supposed to grow
into a mature, stable individual in a variety of children's homes
and with a chain of foster parents.

Over the years I became concerned that perhaps what I was hearing from the mouths of our residents at Yeldall Manor was exceptional. Yet the more I talked with other addicts, the clearer it became that the lack of a secure and loving family life was the major problem in addiction. This was reinforced recently when I came across one particular piece of research concerning a group of fifteen- and sixteen-year-old adolescents, who were asked to report on their perception of their own family relationships. The study concluded, among other things, that:

1 Drug-users were more likely than non-users to perceive their families as distant and less involved. Fathers are more likely to be seen as ineffective, and less significant than mothers. Drug-users reported more parental separation, divorce, remarriage and bereavement.

2 Drug-users reported that they had difficulty in communicating with both parents, and they perceived them as mistrusting, verbally punitive and critical.[1]

Evidence like this is very worrying in the context of what is happening in terms of the breakdown of so many families, especially when we read that Britain has attained the highest divorce rate in Europe. 'One in seven families in Britain has one parent, compared with Europe's average of one in ten.'[2] Commenting on the statistics, Professor Richard Whitfield has stated: 'The indicators for children are appalling in terms of hidden pain and disillusionment.' How many more addicts will there be in the future when we match these facts up with the growing availability of drugs?

All these problems are compounded by the way in which families are increasingly living totally separate lives while dwelling under the same roof. Convenience foods, microwave ovens, and the fact that well over half of all households have two or more televisions, increasingly mean that there is less and less reason for families to relate to one another. This is graphically illustrated by a company in the United States that is doing record business in selling cards that are designed to be left on the breakfast table – they read 'Have a nice day, son'! The implications of living separate, compartmentalised lives where children are not fully loved and cherished can be seen in a story from the thirteenth century. It relates the fact that the ruler, Frederick II, wanted to find out what kind of speech children would have if no one spoke to them in their early days:

> So he bade foster mothers and nurses to suckle the children, to bathe them and wash them, but in no way to prattle with them or to speak to them, for he wanted to learn whether they would speak the Hebrew language, which was the oldest, or Greek, or Latin, or Arabic, or perhaps the language of their parents, of whom they had been born. But he laboured in vain, because the children all died. For they could not live without the petting and the joyful faces and loving words of their foster mothers.

Further confirmation of the need for real love is found in a quote from Peter Farb:

> In 1915 a doctor at the Johns Hopkins Hospital noted that an astounding 90 per cent of the infants admitted to orphanages and foundling homes in Baltimore, Maryland, died within a year – even though they received adequate care. And about three decades ago, a psychoanalytic researcher concluded that an absence of maternal care, stimulation and love lead to physical and emotional retardation and also to a high mortality rate. In fact, thirty-four of the ninety-one foundling-home infants that he studied in the eastern United States and Canada died 'in spite of good food and meticulous medical care'.[3]

Each and every child needs to be loved and cherished. Each and every person needs to grow up in an environment of intimacy that is all about deep and close communion – the security to sit together and talk quietly and comfortably about personal struggles, dreams and aspirations.

Intimacy has been devalued in our society, and needs to be regained to replace what Josh McDowell describes as the counterfeit: 'we were willing to settle for something cheap and empty, albeit very intimate in one way, rather than building long-term relationships that were intimate at several levels; emotional, spiritual, intellectual, social.'[4]

Many of us are the product of homes devastated emotionally by two world wars. Others are part of families that suffered from the 1960s 'me' culture. Yet whatever our background or deprivation, we can choose to be different so that we don't reinforce the insecurity, insignificance and inferiority of another generation.

If all this leaves you depressed by how much needs to be put right in your family, then I can quite understand that. I have had to come face to face with the truth that I was to blame for personally failing to love and cherish my sons adequately in their early years. Yet choosing the discomfort of accepting my own failure and inadequacy was incredibly important in terms of putting things right not only for me, but especially for them. The result is two very mature sons of whom I am immensely proud (in addition to another very special later arrival!).

You *can* change and, in changing, dramatically alter the environment in which the addict or alcoholic in your family can begin to find freedom.

If you have an addict or alcoholic in the family, it may seem to you that the chances of putting things right verge on the miraculous. However, making the choice to be different, to choose the pain and discomfort of meeting other people's needs rather than our own, is infinitely better than wallowing in mediocrity or second-best. Choosing to be a channel for new life, love, hope and intimacy doesn't wipe out past mistakes or deny the hurt we have caused others, but it does offer the powerful and dramatic resource that is so desperately needed by families. The next two chapters look at the practicalities that enable real change to take place.

8

The Practicalities of Breaking Free – Part One

It must be some fourteen years ago that I learnt another very important lesson about helping addicts. It came while walking along a road trying to persuade one young man to return to Yeldall Manor, where he had been living for the last few months. I didn't plead with him to return, but it must have sounded that way. He still kept on walking towards London, and I returned to Yeldall Manor to cope with my anger and frustration over the waste of my time and everyone else's time and, somewhere in it all, my concern about that man and whether he was going to be OK. The lesson that I learnt is very simply and humorously summed up by Dick Schaeffer as 'You sat on the burner, baby ... now you sit on the blisters.'[1] What it means is that every addict has the capacity to accept responsibility for himself or herself. In other words, if you got the 'blisters' by being foolish enough to do something you knew was going to cause you pain, you need to accept responsibility for that, learn from your mistake, and build for the future.

That's what this chapter is all about: creating a family environment, a framework in which the addict or alcoholic can learn to face reality and accept responsibility for his or her own actions. The beauty of it is that it's when addicts begin to learn about accepting responsibility for themselves that they start to take the biggest strides into freedom.

Helping addicts to accept responsibility for their actions

Speaking the truth in love

Addicts often create fantasy lives around themselves. The reason for this is simple: the alternative is to accept life for what it really is – often unfair, unloving, unattractive and boring. It's for this reason that we need to create a home and family environment in which truth and reality prevail. If we don't, then we will continue to reinforce the wrong attitudes in the addict's life and circumstances. It means speaking the truth in love, but not censorially or bitterly – and that's never easy. Speaking the truth in love threatens not only others, but our own security too; however, it's essential if real change is going to take place.

Some time ago I began visiting a particular friend, Anthony, an ex-resident of Yeldall Manor, to help him get back on track after re-using drugs. It was some weeks before I realised he wasn't ready to change. He hadn't made the choice to take responsibility for making changes in relation to his wife, his home and his work – changes that would be uncomfortable, but that were essential for everyone concerned. I had to say to him, with difficulty, 'I hear you saying you want things to be different, but what are you prepared to be and do that is different?' In the end, we agreed that it would be better to continue the counselling at a later date while remaining friends in the meantime.

At the time of writing, Anthony is making dramatic strides, not only in terms of choosing the discomfort of stopping the drugs he was using, but in making those other vital decisions that are resulting in a major, positive difference for his wife, his home and his work situation.

Agreeing on 'bite-sized chunks'

At Yeldall Manor we've learned over the years to help residents do things in 'bite-sized chunks'. For instance, we don't expect a heroin addict to give up cigarette smoking immediately when they arrive. Realism demands that we look at the facts: they are trying to give up a drug that has probably dominated their lives for many years. Once they are through the physical and psychological addiction to heroin, we can help them face up to the issue of giving up tobacco. All this doesn't mean that we allow the addict to do what they want with impunity. Concern for non-smokers in the house, as well as fire hazards, mean that we ask anyone needing to smoke to do it outside.

So don't push too hard for change. Try not to get involved in discussing large life-changing developments too soon. Addicts may well think that changing their job, flat and even their partner is the answer, but your job is to communicate reality. The next appropriate step for them may simply be to buy an alarm clock to help them wake up in the morning, and get to work on time so that their boss doesn't keep giving them a hard time. Instead of changing their accommodation, it may be that addicts need to clean it up or spend time decorating it. In order to begin to put their relationship with their partner right, what they may need to do is simply say sorry!

Allowing them to hit rock-bottom

Every instinct within us, understandably, wants to protect those we love from discomfort or pain. But if you want to see your family member who is addicted find real freedom, then you're going to have to get used to gritting your teeth so that they hit rock-bottom much quicker. The fact of life is that until addicts come to the place where they themselves realise the desperation of their circumstances, they will continue to deny reality, refuse to acknowledge how bad the situation is, and little will change.

It is never easy to refuse a lift to the station to a resident who wants to leave Yeldall Manor, but it's part of the rules. The reason is simple: the mile-long walk to the bus stop has been enough to help many residents accept the fact that they *do* want to face reality in the security of the programme rather than in the harsh world outside. Reality is not a quick fix; it's often a long, painful road. However, it's a road that leads to freedom, not continued addiction.

Breaking your old habits

It will take some time for you to break *your* habits when it comes to helping someone face their responsibilities, but it's worth doing. Only when you sit back and let them come face to face with reality will addicts begin to choose to change. This can apply in the following areas:

- Leaving them to clear up their own vomit.

- Letting them wash their own soiled clothes.

- Letting them phone their boss or school to tell them why they can't come in.

- Allowing them to take responsibility for their lies.

- Leaving them to pay their own fines and deal with their own debts.

- Telling them that they must inform their children why they can't keep a promise.

And if they won't accept responsibility?

If they won't clean up their own vomit, for instance, what do you do? The answer to this depends a great deal on who is affected by their refusal to accept responsibility and their failure to respect others. If it's only you and you feel you can live with the mess, then leave it and give them time to face reality. If there are other members of the family around, then you have responsibilities to them too, and a different response may be appropriate:

- If the vomit is in a shared bedroom, then the other person may need to move out.

- If they won't provide money for housekeeping, then it may be appropriate for them to buy and cook their own food.

- If they won't pay their fines or debts and other people's security is threatened (e.g. if your joint bank account is frozen), then it may be necessary to open a completely separate bank account and even to seek legal advice to protect the other people involved.

When it comes to facing reality, another issue is central: if the addict in the family can get away with things, then what message are you giving to other members of the family, especially children?

Contractual options

Helping addicts face their responsibilities may not only demand some radical steps, but may involve actually working out a written contract between yourself and the addict. It is used in many rehabilitation settings like Yeldall Manor, and is even being used in school and legal situations in the United States to help young people in the early stages of drug and alcohol abuse.

The vitally important issue about a contract is that:

- It cannot be imposed, but is an *agreement* between two parties – you and the person with the drug or alcohol problem.

- It is not only written down, but has a set period in which to operate.

The major reasons for a contract is that it reinforces positive action, and communicates the fact that there is a partnership involvement. Other functions that contracts perform for the addict are as follows:

1 They help to develop a sense of responsibility.

2 They reinforce trust, because everyone has a written agreement to refer to, rather than a vague assumption.

3 They help those involved to be aware of progress or the lack of it.

Implicit in any contract are basic issues that are non-negotiable, including the agreement not to use alcohol or drugs of any description. It should also include what consequences will follow if the contract is broken. It is also vital that a contract is signed by the person who needs to abide by it.

Contracts should also have a limited 'shelf-life', in that if they are entered into positively, they will result in real progress. However, if they are discovered to be too difficult to live with (or even too easy), in that they fail to bring about any change, or cause inappropriate change, then they can be altered. Here is a sample of a basic contract you might use:

I _____ agree to abide by the following conditions from _____ until _____ and I promise that:

1 I will not drink alcohol of any description/I will not use drugs of any description other than those prescribed.

2 I will not verbally or physically abuse anyone.

3 I will attend school between _____ and _____ .

4 I will agree a time to be home on each occasion before leaving the house.

5 I will do my homework before _____ .

Signed _____

Date _____

Consequences

Consequences of not abiding by the agreed rules could include:

- Restricting the times the person is allowed out.
- Refusing access to the family vehicle.

- Limiting television to certain times, e.g. after homework is finished.

- Reducing pocket money or allowance.

These, of course, are only examples, and the agreed consequences need to be tailor-made for the family member and the circumstances. It's also important that, if the contract is continually broken, you will need to review the consequences and think very seriously about making them more uncomfortable. If, on the other hand, there is very real progress in terms of attitudes and action (not just words), then you can write a new contract that reflects this fact.

Contracts are two-way

Contracts should not be one-sided, i.e. so that the addict does all the work. It may be important to draw up a contract that reflects conditions for both parties, e.g. for parents as well as their son/daughter. For instance, it may be appropriate for everyone to agree that:

- No one in the family uses drugs or alcohol.

- There is a specific night each week when everyone stays at home.

- No one is physically or verbally abusive to anyone else.

- Everyone agrees on the amount that each person will provide for housekeeping, etc.

The important issue in all of this is to work together for mutual change, respect and understanding. None of it works through threats or bullying, or because someone promises something they can't realistically deliver. But when it's all been agreed, someone has to pay the cost of making it work – and often that's painful.

How far do you really have to go to bring about real and

lasting change? The answer is summed up in a story told by Gerry Dunn.

A couple who faced a situation of this sort came to me some time ago and asked me to marry them. Although they were both in their fifties, neither had been married before. Moreover, the man was an alcohol addict who had been dry for only six months. I knew him well since I had been counselling him for three years.

'Sally has wanted to marry you for five years,' I reminded him, 'but she has refused because of your drinking. If you are going to get married, there has to be an agreement that you will not drink.' He nodded readily. 'If you take so much as a thimbleful of liquor, you should be out of the house.' Both of them agreed that this was the only basis upon which they could have a happy marriage.

They had been married nine months when Tom took a glass of wine. Tearfully, Sally asked me over the phone, 'What should I do now?'

'You know what the agreement was,' I reminded her.

She packed his clothes and put him out of the house. 'When you're through drinking and ready to try to live a sober life again, you can come back,' she said. 'But not before.'

She threw him out of the house ten different times in two and a half years before he finally yielded to the Lord.

'I was lying on a hospital bed alone,' he said, 'when I realised that there was only one way I could be free. So I said, "God, you take my life."'

Today he has been completely delivered from addiction, and there is joy in that home because a wife stood firm.[2]

I do hope that you don't have to go through the pain described in this story. It isn't an easy process helping someone choose real freedom from addiction, but there's still more you can do to help them – we'll look at this in the next chapter.

9

The Practicalities of Breaking Free – Part Two

Change, in anyone's life, is nearly always gradual rather than immediate or dramatic. A well-planned process can result in long-term, positive change, especially in the case of breaking free from drugs or alcohol. Recognising that this is a process of gradual change, rather than a rapid one, can be liberating for everyone, and can save all involved from unrealistic demands and expectations.

The following process is given as an outline, and it therefore needs to be read, agreed and adapted, preferably by both parties involved. It involves four different phases:

Phase one: thinking about giving up
Phase two: making preparations
Phase three: giving up
Phase four: staying free.

This is not a process that can be forced upon someone, and I would therefore repeat that it's well worth while, at the right time, spending a lot of time discussing how the addict is going to work through the different phases.

Phase one: thinking about giving up

'Risk is the tariff for leaving the Land of Predictable Misery' (Howard Figler).

It is because there are no magic cures or easy answers to addiction that you need to help the addict face the reality of the true cost of giving up drugs or drink. Realism about themselves and their condition is no easy option for addicts to face, and we have to help them to see that it is better than living in a fantasy world where life slowly drains away from them. I don't mean only their physical life drains away, but their mental and spiritual capacity – their whole potential in life – as well. We must help them to see that they have demeaned themselves by their addiction and have denied that which is unique in them; that they are not in control and that much of their life is a sham. They (and we!) also need to learn that giving up drink or drugs is going to be harder than giving up the other things that people get hooked on. Addiction to gambling, sex, pornography or food are difficult enough to break free from, but the drug addict or alcoholic also has to cope with the fact that chemicals are involved. Addicts have to get their head around the fact that when they stop taking the substance, their bodies are going to take time to adjust.

Thinking about giving up means spending time working out the real motives for giving up. If they are giving up for someone else, for instance, then they need to ask themselves whether such a goal will sustain them through the withdrawal. Will doing it for someone else help them cope with everyday life without the drink or a regular fix? Someone giving up because you nag them is not a good result, but talking about what a very real difference it could make to them personally is a different matter. Assisting them to see that being straight will also help others is a part of it too. There's something fulfilling about loving others selflessly, and this can help bring a sense of meaning to their lives.

Phase two: making preparations

No matter how desperate both you and the addict may be for them finally to give up drugs or alcohol, you will both need real patience for phase two. It's all about building foundations; and the more care and time that everyone takes to build those solid foundations, the more likely there is to be real and sustained success.

Phase two is all about changing addicts' thinking as well as taking practical steps. Thinking about all the benefits of giving up is vital, but they can also begin to cut down on the cigarettes, alcohol or drugs, and try reducing their normal intake by a half, a quarter or a tenth every week or every month. Spend time with the addict, getting them to work out options that are realistic and thus stand a much greater chance of sustained success.

Phase two is putting into practice actually saying 'no' rather than talking about it. Addicts can begin by saying, 'No thanks, I really don't want to go out tonight,' or 'I am going to give it a rest tomorrow, so don't call for me.' This phase is all about them really learning to be true to themselves by saying 'no' and *meaning* 'no'. It is going to prepare them, and other people, for the fact that this is a very serious commitment to a drug- or alcohol-free future.

Breaking the fantasy cycle

The addict or alcoholic has a fantasy cycle – just like the rest of us! *Our* fantasy cycle relates to the time when the addict has actually given up drugs and life is going to be completely trouble-free. *Their* fantasy cycle is thinking about their next fix or their next drink, and building it up in their mind to be something really special. Deep down, they know that it's not really going to be that good, but fantasy has become part of their surival routine. Helping them to break their fantasy cycle is helping them to choose to be more realistic about the facts, not the fantasy. It's getting them to talk about the hangovers, the withdrawals, the vomit, the chaos and the confusion. It's patiently helping them to look at the sheer hassle of finding money to pay for their alcohol or drugs, plus the lying, the cheating, always looking over their shoulder. The difficulty for you will be helping them to do that without being condemnatory, and exposing your own frustration at how long it's taking them to break free.

Breaking the fantasy cycle is also about learning that what is submitted to grows stronger, and what is resisted grows weaker. Addicts need you to help them to think about life differently, to convince them that they can actually resist by:

- Working out how they will avoid temptation by keeping away from certain places or specific situations.

- Beginning to mix with different people, and choosing to build relationships with people who are drug- or alcohol-free.

- Going to those services that are available to help them make the decision to stop, e.g. self-help groups.

- Starting to talk differently, on the basis that 'they are what they talk about'.

- Looking honestly at their habits, and getting into different ones, e.g. taking a pride in their appearance.

- Reorganising their diary or timetable so they begin to fill their spare time with more positive things, e.g. keeping fit.

- Starting to take more interest in their work, and how they can do it better.

- Starting to care for others more.

- Taking responsibility for who they are and what they do, instead of blaming everything that's wrong on everyone else.

The final part of phase two is to plan the actual period when they will give up, often called the 'de-tox period' (de-toxification process). In order to ensure that this is as successful as possible, they need help to work out the right time to do it. They may, for instance, need to take time off work or school. They may also need to work out the right time in relation to other activities, i.e. making sure it is not during A-levels. If they have been addicted to drugs or alcohol for more than a year or two, they will need to allow a period of at least two weeks for 'de-tox'. To maximise success, they will also need to consult with a doctor so they can verify the realistic amount of time needed. It will also help if they build up plenty of solid support from yourself and other people who care. Likewise, they will need to learn to ignore anyone who tries to put them off. Furthermore, they may need help to find the right environment in which to go through 'cold turkey'. If they have got their own place, then help them to prepare it well by making it really warm and comfortable. They may not feel like eating to begin with, so make sure the cupboard and fridge contain their favourite 'goodies'. Stock them up with books, tapes and videos (ensuring that there are none which remind them of the 'old' life), and give them a few other treats to make life more enjoyable. Help them particularly to make up their mind to keep the break drug-free (i.e. free from medicinal aids) if it's at all possible. Planning to do it drug-free needs careful thought, but doing it this way will help to avoid a new dependence on, for instance, sleeping tablets. If they have been through 'de-tox' before, they may need a hospital or a clinic, which will need planning well in advance, not least with their GP and local drug agency.

Phase three: giving up

If addicts have prepared themselves well, then they will pick a date to give up and *do it* on that date! Once they have done it, help them to think positively about the new person they have become. Assist them to see that while they may feel lousy, because they are withdrawing, they are also drug-free. If they are not at your home, ensure that you and some positive friends spend lots of time with them, as well as phoning regularly. Work out with them how they can break the time up into one day at a time, or even one hour at a time. Help them to see that they will go through some stages that are more uncomfortable than others, but assure them that these stages don't last for ever. When it comes to thinking positively, help them to think about all the good things they can start to be and do, not least with all the spare time and money they are going to have.

Phase four: staying free

Staying free is not automatic or guaranteed, no matter how long or detailed the preparation period has been. An addict has to keep making the decision to stay free for the rest of his or her life. The one fundamental reason for this is that addicts have discovered a way of experiencing instant pleasure, through drinks or drugs, and that will always be there as an option.

I get really nervous when someone tells me, 'I have cracked it – I am free of drugs and/or drink for ever.' I feel uneasy because phrases like that reinforce the fact that addicts do not realise just how strong the hold is that drugs or drink have over them. They may well be feeling good and confident now, but a few weeks, months or even years down the line they could be feeling low or fed up, and drugs or alcohol could become a valid option once more. Having said this, I would stress that addicts really can be drug- and alcohol-free for the rest of their lives, if they continue to make the choice to be free day by day. I am also convinced that they should *never* drink again if they have been an alcoholic – they *might* get away with it, but I don't think it's worth the risk. Also, I don't think they should drink alcohol if *drugs* were their original problem, for I know too many ex-drug addicts who have gone on to become alcoholics. Whatever their problem, the simple fact of life is that even one drink can lower their inhibitions. One drink simply means that the next drink is easier to accept, and after that it's easier to say, 'Just one more drink' or 'Just one joint.' Addicts need to be strongly encouraged to actively resist any thought of 'controlled' use or the 'I'll have one now and again' routine. All they will do is to maintain or feed the craving mechanism. Giving up completely increases a thousand-fold the chances of them staying free. However, if they do slip up, help them to see the lapse as a reminder of just how vulnerable they really are, and then start afresh.

Whichever phase they are in, I would suggest that you reinforce the need to be very alert to the fact that certain places, faces, written or visual material will trigger a craving. Addicts can't avoid those situations totally, but they can minimise the risks before they happen. It's also important to remind them that temptation rarely comes 'full frontal', but will be much more subtle. It will often begin with a thought, which they can either allow to grow to the point where they are tempted to do something wrong, or get into the routine of replacing it with a much more positive thought. Also, remind them that if they ever start to ask themselves whether it really is worth while being sober, they have got a real problem – and they need to talk to someone urgently.

Danger – from other people

Help addicts to be prepared for the fact that it's often those who care for them the most who may be the most dangerous to their new life, especially after they have been free for a time. People like this will tell them, 'One drink won't matter, after all this time.' Or someone will say, 'Don't offend Fred, have just one drink.' Help them to keep saying NO! The most effective weapon they have is that they know how easily they can slip back into addiction; but if they have forgotten, you may need to remind them that it is as messy down there as it was before, only more so. No addict or alcoholic ever went back into addiction slowly; they always start right back where they finished.

Investment in other people

If it is remotely possible, help your loved one find real fulfilment, when they are ready, by opting to help other people. I never cease to be thankful for the lives of ex-addicts and alcoholics who have reinvested so many wasted years in doing just that. You can't turn the clock back – those men and women always have to live with the consequences of what took place – but although their lives still aren't perfect, there is a quality of purpose, graciousness and strength there that many people who have never touched drugs would be thankful for.

Whatever happens, you as the person helping them will also

change positively – even though you won't always be able to see it. However, you will always need still more wisdom and strength, and the final chapter points you towards finding the resources that *you* need.

10

Choosing Strength out of Weakness (Facing the Truth about Ourselves)

Before you can help the addict in your family effectively, you will probably need to face up to yourself as you really are. To do this can be incredibly painful, because it means admitting your own needs, weaknesses and vulnerability. While this is not easy, choosing to do so means not only that there will be one less casualty, but also that in the long run you will begin to build deep foundations in your own life as well as in the lives of other members of the family. However, I am very much aware that at this point in time you may be in the midst of an ever-growing crisis. It is a crisis which you recognise you have personally contributed to – a view that is reinforced by the addict's manipulation of you in order to achieve his or her ends. You have probably coped with years of being manipulated, lied to, threatened, shouted at, stolen from, cheated, maybe even physically hurt – the list of abuses is endless.

It may be that you have also hurt, desperately, other members of the family you have neglected while seeking to limit what has been happening in the addict's life. You may feel almost totally broken by the grief of that neglect, and by the knowledge of what that could mean for them in the future. Finally, while all that has been going on, you have seen – or are seeing – a husband, wife or child slowly but surely degenerate through their addiction into someone who is a pale shadow of all you hoped and dreamed they would be.

'Co-dependency'

If you're involved in helping someone in your family with an addiction, you will, sooner or later, come across this word. Someone may even have suggested that *you* are 'co-dependent'. What the term implies is that you are too wrapped up in the addict's life for your own well-being. Maybe there's some truth in that for you – and perhaps you do feel uneasy about it. Many of the following criticisms may apply to you: but if they do, it's for very good reasons.

- 'You worry too much about the addict and too little about yourself.' *Yet how else are you supposed to react, as they are your own flesh and blood?*

- 'You believe yourself to be responsible for the feelings and behaviour of others.' *Of course you do; you bore them, brought them up, nurtured them, guided and – apparently – misguided them!*

- 'You are obsessed with controlling other people's behaviour.' *Too right! Anything to stop them destroying their lives!*

- 'You feel guilty and ashamed.' *Of course you do!*

- 'You get angry and resentful.' *What else do people normally do when they are abused?*

- 'You want to cover up problems.' *If you faced them all at once, you would go crazy.*

- 'You avoid family and friends.' *You haven't got the energy to spend time with other people.*

- 'You have medical problems.' *Stress at this level is going to have physical consequences.*

- 'You escape into work and other interests.' *Hardly surprising.*

● 'You are part of the problem.' *Tell me about it!*

Believe me, you're not a freak – you're part of the normal human race and, like everyone with a problem, things get out of proportion. So how do you restore balance so that you can find the security to bring love into the lives of all members of your family?

Balance: dealing with guilt and shame

There are too many people walking around feeling guilty when their problem is not something they did wrong, but something that others did to them. So many of our lives have been powerfully affected by the wrong that other people have done to us, and consequently we have grown up experiencing shame. We are ashamed of so many things – the fact that our father got excessively angry with us; the fact that our mother was a drunkard; the fact that we weren't encouraged or were always put down. Somehow or another we mistook shame for guilt, and we have spent our lives trying to make amends for things that were not our responsibility. On top of all that, we have now replaced shame with guilt because someone in our family is an addict.

It's vitally important to deal with guilt and shame in the right way. *Shame* is dealt with by recognising it for what it really is, and acknowledging that we have no responsibility for it. Dealing effectively with shame also involves accepting the situation for what it is – as we do, it loses its power. We can't do anything about the fact that our mother was a drunkard, but we can choose to accept it rather than deny it. We can choose to accept that we were desperately hurt by our father's anger, rather than carry on assuming it was all our fault. *Guilt* is dealt with by being realistic about something we have done wrong, rather than trying to justify it or rationalise it. Guilt is dealt with by apologising to the person that we've hurt if that's at all possible. It's also defused by choosing to be different and, for some, by seeking a greater source of love.

Balance: in relationships

Right relationships, healthy, dynamic, loving relationships, are at the heart of dealing with problems. Better still, healthy relationships are at the heart of preventing more problems – and especially those relating to drugs and alcohol. Getting relationships right when we are dealing with anyone who is addicted is critical, but never more so than when the addict is a family member. The problem is that one minute we are too close to them, and the next minute, because of certain circumstances, we have distanced ourselves or they have distanced themselves. The problem is exacerbated when we make the decision to stay distanced. 'But,' psychologist James Hammock says, 'if we become disengaged from people, it is because we are enmeshed with something else – because all human beings are made with a need to become involved, to have intimacy.' Accepting that you need the relationship with the addict, and communicating that you want the relationship restored, will bring new hope to you both.

Balance: getting rid of the garbage

If we are going to find freedom for ourselves and the person we are helping, we have to 'bury the past'. In other words, we have to make a conscious decision to cut off completely the negativity of the past, or otherwise it will continue to limit the potential for the future. The writer Floyd McClung once said that the only place to take 'garbage', without its damaging someone else, is to the 'Father heart of God'.[1] When we choose to give over the past in such a way, the future really can be different, because we begin it without the resentment, the anger and the bitterness that have been part of the situation until now.

Balance: the gift of dignity

To ask someone who has coped with an addict in the family to sacrifice more than they have done already is pushing it, and I acknowledge that. But I believe the one thing, above and beyond anything else, that the addict or alcoholic needs is dignity. They need the dignity of being respected as a unique individual who not only has a part to play in the family in the future, but has a positive part to play *now*. Giving them that dignity is not about words, but about sacrificing our right to maintain control. It is about letting them do many things that may result in even more problems for a while, but that's a risk that's worth taking. In researching this book, I came across some words that sum up this role:

> Not to do things for the person I am trying to help, but to be things; not to try to control and change his actions but, through understanding and awareness, to change my reactions. I will change my negatives to positives; fear to faith; contempt for what he does to respect for the potential within him; hostility to understanding; and manipulation or overprotectiveness to release with love, not trying to make him fit a standard or image, but giving him an opportunity to pursue his own destiny, regardless of what his choice may be. I will change my dominance to encouragement; panic to serenity; the inertia of despair to the energy of my own personal growth; and self-justification to self-understanding.[2]

I strongly and passionately believe that *you* are just as important as the addict or alcoholic in your family. I also strongly and passionately believe that out of the tragedy of addiction in your family, you can grow still further into the unique and beautiful person that you were created to be. I believe that because I have faith in a God of love, who seeks to be intimately involved in people's lives through all the tragedy and heartache. I have seen the transformation that has taken place when people have asked God to reveal himself to them, and when they have realised a wonderful truth, a truth well expressed in a story called 'Footprints'.

Footprints

One night I had a dream. I dreamed I was walking along the

beach with God, and across the sky flashed scenes from my life. For each scene I noticed two sets of footprints in the sand; one belonged to me and the other to God.

When the last scene of my life flashed before me I looked back at the footprints in the sand. I noticed that at times along the path of life there was only one set of footprints. I also noticed that it happened at the very lowest and saddest times of my life. This really bothered me and I questioned God about it.

'God, you said that once I decided to follow you, you would walk with me all the way, but I noticed that during the most troublesome times in my life there is only one set of footprints. I don't understand why in times when I needed you most, you would leave me.'

God replied, 'My precious, precious child, I love you and I would never, never leave you during your times of trials and suffering. When you see only one set of footprints it was then that I carried you.'

Anon.

Notes

Chapter 1: The World is a Psychoactive Pic-'n'-Mix Sweet Shop

1 *A Straight Word to Kids*, ed. The Hutterian Brethren (Plough Publishing House, USA, 1987), p. 30.
2 Howard Parker, *Druglink*, November/December 1993.
3 *Alcohol and Drug Abuse Among North West Youth*, University of Manchester, October 1993.
4 John Balding, *Young People in 1992*, Exeter University Health Education Unit, 1993.
5 Bill Hybels, *Christians in a Sex-Crazed Culture* (Victor Books, 1989).

Chapter 2: The Slide into Addiction

1 *Redemption*, April 1987.

Chapter 3: Parent Power – Prevention

1 *The Oxford Times*, 23 July 1993.
2 *The Sunday Times*, 16 October 1994.
3 ibid.
4 Josh McDowell.
5 Lions Club International, *Drug Awareness Programme*.

Chapter 4: Pills, Poppers and Caffeine

1 *Hospital Doctor*, 8 January 1989.
2 Office of Population Censuses and Surveys, 1990.

3 *The Big Blue Book of Booze*, Lifeline and Drinkline, 1994.
4 John Balding, *Young People in 1992*, Exeter University Health Education Unit, 1993.
5 *Drugs and Your Child*, Institute for the Study of Drug Dependence, 1992.
6 *Health Magazine*.
7 Peter Stoker and Mary Brett, *Policing Today*, 1995.
8 Susan Kaplin, 'Research on the "Gateway Effect", Alcohol, Cigarettes and Cannabis', *Life Education International*, March 1994.
9 *Drug Abuse in Scotland*, Scottish Affairs Committee, 1994.
10 *The Sunday Times*, 14 November 1993.

Chapter 5: The Nightmare Scenario

1 *The Sunday Times*, 16 October 1994.

Chapter 7: Family Life and the Addict

1 Ann Stoker and Harith Swadi *Perceived Family Relationship in Drug-Abusing Adolescents* (Elsevier Scientific Publishers Ireland Ltd).
2 Family Policies Study Centre.
3 Peter Farb, *Human Kind*, (Jonathan Cape, 1978).
4 Josh McDowell, *Teens Speak Out* (Scripture Press Foundations Ltd).

Chapter 8: The Practicalities of Breaking Free – Part One

1 Dick Schaeffer, *Choices and Consequences* (Johnson Institute Books, USA), p.8.
2 Gerry Dunn, *God is for the Alcoholic* (Moody Press, USA, 1981), p. 141.

Chapter 10: Choosing Strength out of Weakness

1 Floyd McClung, *The Father Heart of God* (Kingsway, 1985).
2 *Does Someone You Care About Use Drugs?*, Families Anonymous.

UK Resources

National Organisations

Adfam National

The charity for families and friends of drug-users; provides a National Helpline offering information and confidential support; 5th Floor, Epworth House, 35 City Rd, London EC1Y 1AA; tel no: 0171 638 3700.

Al-Anon

Family groups UK and Eire (families and friends of problem drinkers); 61 Great Dover St, London SE1 4YF. Information and details of local group meetings, tel no: 0171 403 0888 (24-hour confidential helpline).

Alateen

For teenagers aged 12–20 whose lives are (or have been) affected by someone else's drinking; tel no: 0171 403 0888.

Alcoholics Anonymous

London tel no: 0171 352 3001 (10 a.m.–10 p.m.) (answerphone other time.) PO Box 1, Stonebow Hse, Stonebow, York YO1 2NJ; tel no: 01904 644026.

Cocaine Anonymous

Answerphone call-back: 0171 284 1123.

Coda (Co-Dependents Anonymous for dysfunctional families)

Information: SAE to Ashburnham Community Centre, Tetcott Rd, London SW10 0SH; tel no: 0171 376 8191.

Drink Line

National Alcohol Helpline; Weddel House, 7th Floor, 13–14 West Smithfield, London EC1A 9DL; tel no (London only): 0171 332 0202; tel no (all UK): 01345 320202.

Families Anonymous

Self-help group for parents/relatives/friends of drug-users that has branches in various parts of the country; tel no: 0171 498 4680; literature given; Rollo Community Assoc., Charlotte Despard Ave, London SW11 15JE; approx 30 UK groups.

Hope UK

Educational and prevention material; 25F Copperfield St, London SE1 0EN; tel no: 0171 928 0848.

ISDD (Institute for the Study of Drug Dependence)

Publishes up-to-date material on various aspects of drug-use; also has a comprehensive library for interested individuals and a research department; Waterbridge House, 32–36 Loman St, London SE1 0EE; tel no: 0171 430 1991.

Life Education Centres

Prevention education for young children aged 3–15 (visit schools with mobile classroom); 10 Southwick Mews, London W2 1JG; tel no: 0171 706 8966.

Life Education Centres

Prevention education for young children aged 3–15 (visit schools with mobile classroom); 20 Long Lane, London EC1A 9HL; tel no: 0171 600 6969.

Narcotics Anonymous

Drug problems; tel no: 0171 272 9040; UK Service office, PO Box 1980, London N19 3LS; literature listings information; helpline: 10 a.m.–10 p.m. weekdays; weekend redirect: 0171 730 0009.

National Drug Prevention Alliance

PO Box 137; London N10 3JJ; c/o tel no: 01753 542296.

Nicotine Anonymous (formerly Smokers Anonymous)

PO Box 1516, London SW1V 4RP; tel no: 0171 233 9241.

Parent Network

44–46 Caversham Rd, London NW5 2DS; tel no: 0171 485 8535.

Positive Prevention Plus

Drug-prevention experts, especially among teenagers; provides resources and training for parents, teachers and youth workers; 3 Radnor Way, Slough, Berks SL3 7LA; tel no: 01753 542296.

Release

Runs a national 24-hour emergency telephone service, particularly useful if someone has been arrested for a drug offence; tel no: 0171 603 8654.

Re-Solv

Deals with glue and other solvents; offers information, advice, teaching materials, research, grants; 30A High St, Stone, Staffs ST15 8AW; tel no: 01785 817885.

SCODA (Standing Conference on Drug Abuse)

Umbrella organisation for drug services; Waterbridge Hse, 32–36 Loman St, London SE1 0EE; tel no: 0171 928 9500

TACADE

Provides education materials, training and information for parents and teachers, and has resources and a consultancy project; 1 Hulme Place, The Crescent, Salford M5 4QA; tel no: 0161 745 8925.

Regional starting points

Avon
Bristol Drug Project
18 Guinea St
Redcliffe
Bristol
BS1 6SX
Tel no: 01179 298047

Bedfordshire
Luton Drug Helpline
34 Clarendon Rd
Luton
LU2 7PQ
Tel no: 01582 32200

Berkshire (East)
East Berkshire District Drugs Team
Oak House
Upton Hospital
Albert St
Slough
SL1 2BJ
Tel no: 01753 821789

Berkshire (West)
The Drug Unit and Neutral Zone
Drug Unit Service
156 Oxford Rd
Reading
RG1 7PJ
Tel no: 01734 391452

Buckinghamshire
Buckingham Council on Alcohol and Drugs
Bierton Rd
Aylesbury
HP20 1EU
Tel no: 01296 25329

Cambridgeshire
Bridge Project
154 Mill Rd
Cambridge
CB1 3LP
Tel no: 01223 214 614

Cheshire
Cheshire Drugs and Training and Information Centre
Suite 'B'
Theatre Court
London Rd
Northwich
CW9 5HB
Tel no: 01606 49055

Cleveland
Drug Advice and Counselling Centre
63 Kings Rd
North Ormsby
Middlesbrough
TS3 6EP
Tel no: 01642 242550

Cornwall
Freshfields Service
10 Strangway Terrace
Truro
TR1 2NY
Tel no: 01872 41952

Cumbria
Dependency Service
Croft House
Wigton Rd
Carlisle
CA1 3FP
Tel no: 01228 49605

Derbyshire
Derby Drugline (Turning Point)
2nd Floor
Willow House
Willow Rd
Derby
DE1 3NZ
Tel no: 01332 382954

Devon
Exeter Drugs Project
59 Magdalen St
Exeter
EX2 4HY
Tel no: 01392 410292

Dorset (East)
East Dorset Drug and Alcohol Advice Square
Bungalow 6
Royal Victoria Hospital
Gloucester Rd
Boscombe
Bournemouth
BH7 6JE
Tel no: 01202 304455

Dorset (West)
Community Alcohol and Drugs Advisory Service
28 High West St
Dorchester
DT1 1UP
Tel no: 01305 269099

Durham
North East Council on Addictions
Durham Alcohol and Drug Advisory Centre
Shakespeare Hall
North Road
Durham
DH1 45Q
Tel no: 0191 3830331

Essex
NEEDAS
1 Hospital Rd
Colchester
CO3 3HJ
Tel no: 01206 48481

Gloucestershire
Gloucestershire Drug Project
24 Cambray Place
Cheltenham
GL50 1JN
Tel no: 01242 570003

Greater Manchester
Lifeline Project
Globe House
Southall St
Manchester
M3 1LG
Tel no: 0161 8392054

Hampshire
Drugs Advice Centre
Northern Rd
Cosham
Portsmouth
PO6 3EP
Tel no: 01705 324636

Herefordshire
Hereford Community Drug Service
27A Owens St
Hereford
HR1 3JB
Tel no: 01432 263636

Isle of Wight
Community Drug and Alcohol Team
50 Carisbrooke Rd
Newport
PO30 1BU
Tel no: 01983 526654

Kent
Druglink
The Hollies
Stonehouse Hospital
Dartford
DA2 6AU
Tel no: 01322 91702

Leicestershire
Leicestershire Community Drug Services and Drug Advice
  Centre
Paget House
2 West St
Leicester
LE1 6XP
Tel no: 01162 470200

London (Central)
Hungerford Drug Project
32a Wardour St
London
W1V 3HJ
Tel no: 0171 437 3523

London (East)
Community Drug Advice Service
Oxlow Lane Clinic
Oxlow Lane
Dagenham
RM10 7YU
Tel no: 0181 592 7748

London (North)
Drug Concern Barnet (Barnet Drug and Alcohol Service)
Woodlands
Colindale Hospital Grounds
London
NW9 5HG
Tel no: 0181 200 9525

London (South East)
Community Drug Project
30 Manor Place
London
SE17 3BB
Tel no: 0171 703 0559

London (South West)
Kaleidoscope Project
40–46 Cromwell Rd
Kingston-upon-Thames
KT2 2RE
Tel no: 0181 549 2681

London (West)
The Blenheim Project
7 Thorpe Close
London
W10 5XL
Tel no: 0181 960 5599

Merseyside
Mersey Drug Training and Information Centre
The Liverpool Palace
Slater St
Liverpool
L1 4BW
Tel no: 0151 709 3511

Norfolk
Community Alcohol and Drug Service
4 Avenue Rd
Kings Lynn
PE30 5NW
Tel no: 01553 761623

Nottinghamshire
John Storer Clinic
Amberley St
Nottingham
NG1 6HD
Tel no: 01159 418964

Oxfordshire
Department of Addictive Behaviour
Chilton Clinic
Warneford Hospital
Oxford
OX3 7JX
Tel no: 01865 226243

Shropshire
Drug Help
3 Haygate Rd
Wellington
Telford
TF1 1QX
Tel no: 01952 222229

Somerset
Somerset Council on Alcohol and Drugs
3 Upper High St
Taunton
TA1 3PX
Tel no: 01823 288174

Staffordshire
Woton House
St George's Hospital
Corporation St
Stafford
ST16 3AG
Tel no. 01785 57888 (Ext. 5031)

Suffolk (East)
Community Drug Team
40 Bond St
Ipswich
IP4 1JE
Tel no: 01473 236069

Suffolk (West)
West Suffolk Drug Advisory Service
18 St John's St
Bury St Edmunds
IP33 1SJ
Tel no: 01284 762377

Surrey
Surrey Alcohol and Drug Advisory Service
21 Kingsway
Woking
GU21 1NU
Tel no: 01483 755914

Sussex (East)
Brighton Drug Dependency Clinic
Herbert Hone Clinic
11 Buckingham Rd
Brighton
BN1 3RA
Tel no: 01273 23395

Sussex (West)
Substance Abuse Service
Crawley Hospital
West Green Drive
Crawley
RH11 7DH
Tel no: 01293 551134

Tyne and Wear
North East Council on Addictions
NECA HQ
1 Mosley St
Newcastle-upon-Tyne
NE1 1YE
Tel no: 0191 2320797

Warwickshire
Drug Advisory Service
109 Warwick St
Leamington Spa
CV32 4QZ
Tel no: 01926 316817

West Midlands
Birmingham Drugline
Dale House
New Meeting St
Birmingham
B4 7SX
Tel no: 0121 632 6363

Wiltshire
Druglink Advisory Centre
174 Victoria Rd
Swindon
SN1 3DF
Tel no: 01793 610133

Worcestershire
Worcestershire Druglink
The Angel Centre
Angel Place
Worcester
WR1 3QW
Tel no: 01905 724853

Yorkshire (North)
York Drug Resources Scheme
74 Skeldergate
York
YO1 1DN
Tel no: 01904 647474

Yorkshire (South)
Rockingham Drug Project
117 Rockingham St
Sheffield
S1 4EN
Tel no: 01142 580033

Yorkshire (West)
The Bridge Project
40 Piccadilly
Bradford
BD1 3NN
Tel no: 01274 723863

Northern Ireland
Shaftesbury Square Hospital
116–122 Great Victoria St
Belfast
BT2 7BG
Tel no: 01232 329 808

Scotland
Scottish Drugs Forum
5 Oswald St
Glasgow
G1 5QR
Tel no: 0141 221 1175
(Drugline Scotland: 0800 776 8711)

Wales
All Wales Drugline
1 Neville St
Cardiff
CF1 8LP
Tel no: 01222 383313

Residential rehabilitation (Christian projects)

Arbour, The
16 The Chase
Clapham
London
SW4 0NH
Tel no: 0171 498 2423

Caleb House
21 Victoria Rd
Clevedon
Avon
BS21 7RU
Tel no: 01275 341112

Coke Hole Trust
20A Bridge St
Town Mills House
Andover
Hampshire
SP10 1BL
Tel no: 01264 361745

Hebron House
12 Stanley Ave
Thorpe Hamlet
Norwich
Norfolk
NR7 0BE
Tel no: 01603 39905

Kenward Trust
Kenward House
Kenward Rd
Yalding
Kent
ME18 6AH
Tel no: 01622 81260

Langley House Trust
Chatterton Hey
Edenfield
Ramsbottom
Lancashire
BL0 0QH
Tel no: 0170 682 4554

Manna Farm Project
Old Rufford Rd
Calverton
Nottingham
NG14 6NW
Tel no: 01602 654001

Murray Lodge
Whitley Village
Coventry
West Midlands
CV3 4AJ
Tel no: 01203 501585

Safety Net Project
Yeldall Manor
Blakes Lane
Hare Hatch
Reading
RG10 9XR
Tel no: 01734 401093

Spitalfield Crypt Trust
22a Hanbury St
London
E1 6QR
Tel no: 0171 247 7766

Teen Challenge
52 Penygroes Rd
Gorslas
Llanelli
Dyfed
SA14 7LA
Tel no: 01269 842718

Willowdene Farm
Chorley
N. Bridgnorth
Shropshire
WV16 6PP
Tel no: 01746 32658

Yeldall Manor
Blakes Lane
Hare Hatch
Reading
RG10 9XR
Tel no: 01734 404411

Day services/counselling

Alcoholics Victorious
26 Mason Rd
Stroud
Gloucestershire
GL6 1HT
Tel no: 01453 762263
Works with alcoholics, drug-users and their families, including a weekly support group

Amethyst Centre for Alcohol Concern
207 London Rd
Reading
Berkshire
RG1 3NT
Tel no: 01734 663339
Alcohol and drug-prevention education in schools, churches, youth and adult groups. Advice in setting up alcohol-free bars

Centrepoint Outreach
2A Tower St
Boston
Lincolnshire
PE21 8RX
Tel no: 01205 360900
Drop-in centre for those with addiction and other problems, including support service for parents

Crisis Centre, The
12 City Rd
Bristol
Avon
BS2 8TP
Tel no: 01272 423088
Drop-in centre with training in life skills and access to employment courses

Daybreak Drug Abuse Project
St Luke's Church Centre
Dagenham Rd
Dagenham
Essex
RM10 7UP
Tel no: 0181 595 2010

Help Counselling Services
118 Wood Lane
Chippenham
Wiltshire
SN5 3DZ
Tel no: 01225 767459
Confidential counselling on problems with drugs, alcohol and tranquillisers, AIDS and homelessness

Kestrel
44 Merryhill Rd
Bracknell
Berks
RG12 2DP
Tel no: 01734 568850
Addicts' support group

Life for the World Trust
Wakefield Building
Gomm Rd
High Wycombe
Bucks
HP13 7DJ
Tel no: 01494 462008
Discipleship – counselling/work/education programme

Lifeline
84 Hazebrouck Rd
Faversham
Kent
ME13 7RN
Tel no: 01795 534971
Advice to schools, churches, etc., on substance abuse. Supports those with addiction problems

Matthew Project, The
24 Pottergate
Norwich
Norfolk
NR2 1DX
Tel no: 01603 626123
Street agency, 24-hour helpline and mobile service offering counselling advice, information and help to drug-users and families

Overcomers
PO Box 102
Bracknell
Berkshire
RE12 5YX
Tel no: 01344 52135
A 12-step recovery programme (biblically based). Involves a 90-day daily choice working manual with local group meetings for teaching, support and group work

Philippi House
34 Sherbourne Rd
Blackpool
Lancashire
FY1 2PW
Tel no: 01253 21859
Teaching and training counsellors to respond to problems of addiction and all forms of misuse

Tranquillisers Freedom Line (John 10:10 Trust)
Manor Park Christian Centre
454 High St North
Manor Park
London
E12 6RH
Tel no: 0181 470 9930
Telephone helpline for those wanting to come off tranquillisers. Training and information offered to those seeking to help others

Wirral Christian Drugs Action
18A Oxton Rd
Birkenhead
Merseyside
L42 2QJ
Tel no: 051 647 5134
Works directly with drug-misusers; also carries out drug-prevention education in schools, etc.

USA Resources

Addiction Research Foundation

Marketing Services, 33 Russell St, Toronto, Ontario M5S 2S1, Canada; tel no: (416) 595-6056.

Al-Anon Family Group

1372 Broadway, New York, NY 10018-0862; tel no: (212) 302-7240.

Alateen

1372 Broadway, New York, NY 10018-0862; tel no: (212) 302-7240.

Alcoholics Anonymous

General Service Office, PO Box 459, Grand Central Station, New York, NY 10163; tel no: (212) 686-1100.

American Council for Drug Education

204 Monroe St, Rockville, MD 20850; tel no: (301) 294-0600.

American Medical Society on Alcoholism and Other Drug Dependencies

12 West St, 7th Floor, New York, NY 10010; tel no: (212) 206-6770.

Codependents Anonymous Inc.

PO Box 33577, Phoenix, Arizona 85067; tel no: (602) 944 0141.

Families Anonymous

World Services Office Inc., PO Box 528, Van Nuys, CA 91408; tel no: (818) 989 7841.

Families in Action Drug Information Center

Suite 300, 3845 N. Druid Hills Rd, Decatur, GA 30033; tel no: (404) 325-5799.

Johnson Institute

7151 Metro Boulevard, Minneapolis, MN 55435; tel no: (612) 944-0511.

Mothers against Drunk Driving

National Headquarters, 669 Airport Freeway, Suite 310, Hurst, Texas, TX 76053-3944; tel no: (817) 268-6233.

Narcotics Anonymous

World Services Office Inc., PO Box 999, Van Nuys, CA 91409; tel no: (818) 780-3951.

National Association of Addiction Treatment Programs, Inc.

2082 Michelson Drive, Suite 304, Irvine, CA 92715; tel no: (714) 476-8204.

National Association of Alcoholics

31706 Coast Highway, Suite 201, South Laguna, CA, USA; tel no: (714) 499-3889.

National Association of State Alcohol and Drug Abuse Directors Inc.

444 North Capitol St, NW, Suite 520, Washington, DC 20001; tel no: (202) 783-6868.

National Black Alcoholism Council

417 South Dearborn, Suite 700, Chicago, IL 60605; tel no: (312) 341-9466.

National Clearinghouse for Alcohol and Drug Information

1776 East Jefferson St, Rockville, MD 20852; tel no: (301) 468-2600.

National Clergy Council on Alcoholism

1200 Varnum St, NE, Washington, DC 20017; tel no: (202) 832-3811.

National Coalition for the Prevention of Drug and Alcohol Abuse

Quest International, 6655 Sharon Woods Blvd, Columbus, OH 43229; tel no: (614) 882-6400.

National Congress of Parents and Teachers (PTA)

700 North Rush St, Chicago, IL 60611-2571; tel no: (312) 787-0977.

National Federation of Parents for Drug-Free Youth

8730 Georgia Ave, Suite 200, Silver Spring, MD 20910; tel no: 1-800-554-KIDS.

National Institute on Drug Abuse

Room 10-05, Parklawn Building, 5600 Fishers Lane, Rockville, MD 20857; tel no: (301) 443-4577.

Office for Substance Abuse Prevention

Room 13A54, Parklawn Building, 5600 Fishers Lane, Rockville, MD 20857.